LIZARDS
OF AUSTRALIA

LIZARDS OF AUSTRALIA

STEPHEN SWANSON

ANGUS
& ROBERTSON

AN ANGUS & ROBERTSON BOOK

First published in Australia by Angus & Robertson Publishers in 1976
Reprinted in 1980
Revised and enlarged edition 1987
This revised edition published by Collins/Angus & Robertson
Publishers Australia in 1990

Collins/Angus & Robertson Publishers Australia
Unit 4, Eden Park, 31 Waterloo Road, North Ryde
NSW 2113, Australia

William Collins Publishers Ltd
31 View Road, Glenfield, Auckland 10, New Zealand

Angus & Robertson (UK)
16 Golden Square, London W1R 4BN, United Kingdom

Copyright © Stephen Swanson 1976, 1987

National Library of Australia
Cataloguing-in-Publication data

Swanson, Stephen.
  Lizards of Australia.

  Rev. ed.
  Includes index.
  ISBN 0 207 15381 7.

  1. Lizards — Australia — Identification. I.Title.
  (Series: Australian natural science library).

597.95'0994

Cover photograph: Boyd's Forest Dragon (Gonyocephalus boydii)
Printed in Singapore

8   7   6   5   4
95   94   93   92   91   90

Preface

In preparing this book I have tried to refrain from excessive use of confusing terminology: however, owing to the conflicting nature of common names, which generally differ from one locality to another, it has been necessary to identify each lizard with the appropriate scientific name according to zoological classification. A detailed description of each lizard has been unnecessary, since the colour photographs are adequate for this purpose. With few exceptions the lizards photographed in this book have been collected by myself or in my presence, and the location of collection accompanies each photograph. The chapters "Lizards in Captivity" and "Photographing Lizards" are the result of my personal experiences in this field. I hope the suggestions made will help to alleviate many of the pitfalls that face the beginner.

For his assistance during the preparation of this book I am particularly indebted to Graeme Gow, without whose influence it would not have been attempted. I am also grateful to Graeme and other friends Gunther Schmida, Paul Horner, John Cann, Peter Krauss, John Rigby and Grant Husband for their company on collecting trips and assistance while photographing many difficult subjects.

If men were as much men as lizards are lizards
they'd be worth looking at.

D. H. LAWRENCE

Contents

Introduction

Lizards are reptiles and therefore cold-blooded; that is, they rely upon heat from an external source to regulate the temperature of their body. With the exception of a few specialised forms, it is a relatively easy process to separate the lizards from the remaining three groups of reptiles inhabiting the Australian continent. The lack of a bony shell encasing the body allows for immediate differentiation between the lizards and Testudines (tortoises and turtles); some confusion may arise, however, from a superficial resemblance which certain species bear to the snakes and crocodiles.

Although outwardly similar in general appearance to the typical lizard, the crocodile differs to a remarkable degree in anatomical features. In addition to the large number of internal differences in the skeletal structure and the circulatory system, there are two obvious external features of the crocodile by which identification may be determined. They are the anal cleft, which unlike that of the lizard is vertically positioned, and the tongue, which, far from being the flexible and highly specialised organ of the lizard, is firmly anchored to the lower jaw, being practically immovable.

Since they share the same order with the snakes (Squamata), lizards are more closely related to these than to the crocodiles or Testudines. Although the typical lizard is immediately distinguished from the snake in having four well-developed limbs, movable eyelids and visible ear openings, there are a number of notable exceptions in which the limbs are either completely or partially absent, visible ear openings are non-existent, or the eye is covered with a fixed transparent scale. The key in determining the true status of the lizard or snake lies with the highly specialised structure and function of the snake's lower jaw. The union of the two halves of the lower jaw in the lizard is permanent, but in the snake these are joined by an elasticised ligament that allows for distension to swallow animals appreciably larger than its own head.

The necessity of adaptation to a highly variable terrain has produced an amazing variety of lizards, which in diversity of size, form and colour are perhaps unmatched by any other group of Australian fauna. Australian lizards range in size from a number of skinks and geckos considered full grown at a length of 7 centimetres, to the Perenty (*Varanus giganteus*) of central Australia, occasionally attaining a length of 2½ metres. The extent of diversification in form could be most effectively illustrated by taking a comparison between certain burrowing skinks, whose subterranean habits have resulted in an elongation of the body and partial or complete degeneration of the limbs, and the Thorny Devil (*Moloch horridus*) of central Australia whose entire body is adorned with spiky protuberances. The primary factor in determining the colouration of the majority of lizards tends to be camouflage. Many species, such as the Inland Bearded Dragon (*Pogona vitticeps*), become very difficult to detect when motionless amid natural surroundings. There are a number of strikingly marked exceptions to this rule, their colouring apparently acting as a deterrent to predators.

Some Australian lizards, particularly dragons, have the ability to change colour to a restricted degree during emotional disturbances. These colour changes may take place during temperature variation, sexual activity, or when the lizard is in an agitated, sick or injured state.

Lizards are represented in all regions of the continent, from the desert areas of central Australia to the tropical rainforests of north-eastern Queensland. The majority are terrestrial, carrying out all the basic functions of life on the ground, and dwelling in a burrow or beneath rocks and fallen timber. Certain species live entirely among rock outcrops, the crevices of which afford sufficient shelter from the elements and protection from predators to which they would otherwise fall an easy victim. A number of specialised forms lead a subterranean existence, burrowing in soft, sandy soil and rarely making an appearance on the surface. Few are strictly arboreal as is Gillen's Pigmy Monitor (*Varanus gilleni*), a strongly clawed species from the central Australian region, but many which spend much of their time on the ground take advantage of the protection afforded by the hollow limbs of a tree when seeking shelter. There are a small number of semiaquatic varieties, spending most of the time in or beside the water, but few which show the amount of adaptation to this particular habitat as does Merten's Water Monitor (*Varanus mertensi*) of northern Australia. The tail is vertically compressed to aid progression in the water, and the nostrils, which are located on top of the snout, are equipped with valves, enabling the lizard to remain submerged for extended periods.

The majority of lizards are diurnal — active during the daylight hours. A large number, however, are nocturnal, remaining concealed during the day and emerging only after dark. A few species vary in this respect, depending on the climatic zone in which they occur. Many that are diurnal in temperate areas tend to be most active on warm nights in the tropical or desert regions. In cold climates lizards enter into hibernation during the winter months, remaining concealed beneath rock, fallen timber or any other shelter that offers sufficient protection from the frost.

Australian lizards are primarily carnivorous in their feeding habits, devouring insects, worms, snails, fish, crustaceans, amphibians, other reptiles, birds, and mammals, in appropriate relation to their size. A number of species also feed on a variety of native plants, but none is completely vegetarian. Lizards periodically shed the outer layer of their skin, the frequency of this occurrence depending largely on the rate of growth, age, and health of each individual. The discarded skin, which is worked loose against rocks or other suitable projections, is usually shed in pieces, though it may occasionally be cast entire. A large proportion of lizards, notably the geckos, skinks, and legless lizards, have the ability to cast off their tail when seized by a predator. The violent contractions of the dismembered portion often hold the attention of the predator momentarily, thus enabling the lizard to escape unnoticed. Regeneration of the tail will result within a variable length of time, but the new section will lack the perfect proportion and colouration of the original. Tail loss in dragon and monitor lizards, however, results in a permanent stumped tail. Partial regeneration may occur with some dragons, the newly grown member being devoid of scales.

As a rule, lizards lay eggs; these are deposited among decaying vegetation or timber, beneath rocks, or in a hole scooped in sandy soil. Upon completing this task, females show no apparent concern for the welfare of their eggs, leaving them entirely unattended. The period of incubation may be anything from six weeks to occasionally ten months, depending upon temperature, humidity, and the species concerned. The young emerge from the shell with the aid of a sharp projection on the snout known as the egg tooth, and are generally replicas of their parents, though usually more distinctly marked. A minority of species, notably the larger skinks, give birth to live young encased in a transparent yolk sac which ruptures at birth. A few varieties represent an intermediate stage between the egg-laying and live-bearing species; the eggs of such lizards contain fully developed young which usually hatch within a few days of being deposited.

There are no venomous lizards in Australia, the only two venomous species in the world being confined to the United States of America and Mexico. Although a bite from one of the larger monitors may result in severe lacerations, the majority are quite harmless, and all species invariably choose to retreat if given this alternative.

Members of the suborder Sauria (lizards) are represented in Australia by five distinct families.

Geckos

The geckos (Gekkonidae) are distributed throughout all climatic regions of Australia. They are unimpressive in size, the largest, the Leaf-tailed Gecko (*Phyllurus cornutus*) of north-eastern Queensland attaining a maximum length of only 25 centimetres while the majority are full grown at 10 centimetres. Owing to the lack of overlapping scales typical of most lizards, the geckos present a somewhat fragile appearance. Although the soft skin is often studded with tubercles, this affords the gecko little protection. The eyes are large, and in all species covered with a fixed transparent disc, which is cleaned regularly with the aid of the tongue.

All Australian varieties are nocturnal, sheltering during the day beneath the loose bark of trees, within rock crevices, under fallen timber, or in a burrow in sandy soil. The tail is easily cast off when the owner is molested; it is in fact uncommon for mature individuals of many species to possess an original tail. Many of the climbing varieties are equipped with highly developed pads on the digits of all limbs, which enable the gecko to move effortlessly upon smooth surfaces such as walls and ceilings.

The geckos are invariably insectivorous in their feeding habits, though a number of the larger species, such as the Central Knob-tailed Gecko (*Nephrurus levis levis*), prey upon smaller geckos and skinks. All are oviparous, usually producing only two or three eggs to the clutch.

Legless Lizards

The Pygopodidae is the only family unique to the Australasian region, all its members being found within Australia and New Guinea alone. In all forms the body is elongate and lacking in apparent limbs, presenting a somewhat snake-like appearance. They do, however, possess the remnants of hind limbs, in the form of faintly discernible flaps which are usually held firmly against the body on either side of the vent.

The largest member is the Common Scaly Foot (*Pygopus lepidopodus*), a mature specimen of which, with an original tail, may measure 75 centimetres in length. The tail in the majority of species is of considerable length, and highly prone to dismemberment.

The legless lizards have a transparent scale covering the eyes, as do snakes, but may be distinguished from the latter in having a broad, fleshy tongue, and, with rare exceptions, detectable ear openings. The majority are insectivorous, but Burton's Legless Lizard (*Lialis burtonis*) feeds upon skinks, geckos, and occasionally small snakes. All members of this highly developed family are terrestrial, living on the ground beneath logs, rocks, or in the central regions amongst porcupine grass. A number of species are subterranean, certain members of this group being amongst Australia's rarest reptiles.

Legless lizards are oviparous, the eggs being rather elongate, and usually numbering only two or three to the clutch.

5

Dragons

Within this group, the Agamidae, will be found a number of varieties which are undoubtedly amongst our most conspicuous forms. All are typically lizard-like in appearance and many are furnished with an impressive array of spines, or such spectacular adornment as the "frill" of the Frilled Lizard (*Chlamydosaurus kingii*) of northern Australia.

While the majority are terrestrial, living on the ground within a burrow or rock crevice, a large number are skilled climbers, spending the greater part of the day in the trees, and a few are semiaquatic, retiring to the safety of the water when alarmed. All species are strictly diurnal, being active only during the day, when they feed upon almost any live food available, and occasionally native plants.

Dragons are second in size only to the monitors, the largest being the Eastern Water Dragon (*Physignathus lesueurii lesueurii*) which occasionally attains a length of one metre. A number of species develop a bipedal gait when pursued, raising the forebody from the ground and progressing with the aid of the hind limbs alone.

Many dragons participate in an elaborate courtship display during the mating season, with such unexplainable phenomena as "arm-waving" and "head-bobbing" taking place. All are oviparous, the number of eggs produced differing between the species.

Monitors

Australia may justifiably be referred to as the home of the monitors (Varanidae), for there is greater proliferation of this family in Australia than in any other region of the world. All are strictly carnivorous, being noted for their voracious feeding habits. The monitors, or goannas as they are more frequently called in Australia, show remarkable diversity in size, though in general appearance they are all strikingly similar. They range in size from the Short-tailed Monitor (*Varanus brevicauda*), full grown at 20 centimetres, to the Perenty (*Varanus giganteus*), which sometimes attains a length of 2½ metres. Perhaps the most notable feature is the tongue, which is forked, and protruded regularly in a similar manner to that of the snake. Showing successful adaptation to a highly variable terrain, the monitors are represented throughout Australia, with the exception of

Tasmania. The majority shelter in a burrow or rock crevice, but many live in the trees within hollow limbs. Many species are skilled climbers, and all are capable swimmers, a number being markedly semiaquatic in habit.

All monitors lay eggs, and the period of incubation is often of considerable length in comparison to that of other lizards.

Skinks

The skinks (Scincidae) are undoubtedly the most successful family of lizards in Australia, and are perhaps the most successful in the world. The majority are smooth in appearance with four functional limbs and movable eyelids, but there are a number of notable exceptions. Owing to their subterranean habits, many burrowing forms have suffered a complete or partial degeneration of the limbs, while others have a fixed transparent scale covering the eye. With few exceptions the tail is long and easily cast. The regeneration process sometimes results in more than one tail being produced from the stump of the original. Although the majority of skinks are carnivorous, a large number are omnivorous, consuming plant as well as animal food.

The largest and most powerful member of this group is the Land Mullet (*Egernia major*) from the coastal forests of northern New South Wales and southern Queensland.

Within this widespread group are the only Australian lizards capable of producing live young, although this is the exception rather than the rule. The production of live young is more noticeable amongst the larger forms, while the majority lay eggs as do all members of the other families in Australia.

The Lizards Described

GECKOS
Gekkonidae

Clawless Gecko *Crenadactylus ocellatus*   **Plate   1**

The Clawless Gecko ranges throughout the deserts of western and central Australia.

This diminutive gecko, fully grown at 8 centimetres, is an inhabitant of porcupine grass thickets.

Banded Gecko *Cyrtodactylus louisiadensis*   **Plate   2**

This gecko sometimes reaches a length of 25 centimetres, and is one of Australia's largest. It occurs in north-eastern Queensland and is also found in New Guinea. It is shy and uncommon, concealing itself within crevices in rock outcrops during the day. It has also been found amongst timber and in abandoned houses.

The Banded Gecko has been recorded as feeding on insects and small mice, which it quickly subdues with its relatively powerful jaws.

Byrne's Gecko *Diplodactylus byrnei*   Plate 3

A small, terrestrial lizard, Byrne's Gecko is fully grown at a length of 9 centimetres.

It occurs in arid regions from central Australia to western New South Wales. It ventures from its subterranean abode at night, to forage on the sandy plains for small insects.

Spiny-tailed Gecko *Diplodactylus ciliaris*   Plates 4A, 4B

One of the most spectacular and brightly coloured of the Australian geckos, the Spiny-tailed Gecko is distributed throughout a great deal of northern and central Australia. Individual specimens may be reddish or grey in colour, depending largely upon the area in which they occur. It has the ability to vary the intensity of its colouration to a marked degree, but the reason behind this behaviour is obscure, since it is nocturnal in habit and therefore, unlike many of the diurnal lizards, has little reason to conform to its surroundings as a means of camouflage.

From the large percentage of adults encountered with an original tail, it appears that this lizard differs from many other geckos in being reluctant to part with this appendage. The regenerated tail is easily distinguished, being covered with shorter, irregular spines over the entire surface.

During the daylight hours the Spiny-tailed Gecko is inactive, concealing itself in hollow tree limbs, beneath the loose bark of trees or under exfoliating rock. The maximum size attained is 13 centimetres.

Fat-tailed Gecko *Diplodactylus conspicillatus*   Plate 5

This small gecko is abundant in the drier areas of northern and central Australia. Its most noteworthy feature is the short, thick tail which it uses to block access to the burrow into which it retires during the day.

It appears to be somewhat unpopular as an addition to the diet of a predator, but when seized it will increase its size by inflating with air, thus making itself more difficult to swallow. It attains a maximum length of only 7 centimetres and feeds upon small insects.

Jewelled Gecko *Diplodactylus elderi* Plate 6

This attractive lizard lives among dense porcupine grass thickets in red-soil regions of central Australia and surrounding districts. As well as providing shelter and protection, the porcupine grass offers a constant supply of food in the form of innumerable insects which also take advantage of the shelter afforded by this plant.

The Jewelled Gecko grows to only 7 centimetres in length, and is capable of exuding a sticky substance from its tail when disturbed.

Steindachner's Gecko *Diplodactylus steindachneri* Plate 7

This beautifully marked gecko occurs in dry areas of Queensland and western New South Wales. It retires beneath the ground during the day, but can be found on the surface after dark where it is active in pursuit of the small insects upon which it feeds.

Its dorsal markings can be variable, the even pattern occasionally being broken up into irregular blotches. Steindachner's Gecko grows to slightly over 7 centimetres in length.

Crowned Gecko *Diplodactylus stenodactylus* Plate 8

This small gecko is found from central Australia to the north of Western Australia and the Northern Territory. The dorsal patterning is variable amongst individual specimens, the regular reticulations often giving way to irregular cross-bands or a vertebral stripe. The Crowned Gecko shelters beneath the ground or occasionally amongst porcupine grass during the day, and grows to about 7 centimetres in length.

White-striped Gecko *Diplodactylus taeniatus* Plate 9

This peculiar gecko shows perhaps a greater degree of adaptation to its habitat than any other species. The unusual markings and slender body render it virtually undetectable amongst the porcupine grass where it chooses to make its home. During the day it remains motionless, in a vertical position with the head pointing down and the stripes on its body running parallel to the needles of the grass. If its elaborate camouflage fails, the White-striped Gecko is equally well equipped with means of defence. When threatened it may open its mouth widely, displaying a bright orange interior, and on being seized will exude a sticky substance from pores on the tail.

It preys on small insects which abound amongst the thick bush, where it moves about with an agility equal to that of other geckos on the ground. The tail is prehensile, aiding the lizard in securing a firm grip in such difficult surroundings. The White-striped Gecko grows to a length of about 7 centimetres and occurs in desert and semidesert areas from the Mount Isa district of Queensland to north-western Australia.

Golden-tailed Gecko *Diplodactylus taenicauda*   Plate 10

The Golden-tailed Gecko is an arboreal gecko inhabiting the Darling Downs district and adjacent areas of south-eastern Queensland. It is easily recognised by the distinctive russet stripe on the dorsal surface of the tail. When seized it releases a sticky, toxic liquid from the tail in an effort to repel its aggressor.

The Golden-tailed Gecko measures approximately 11 centimetres in length.

Tesselated Gecko *Diplodactylus tesselatus*   Plate 11

A small burrowing gecko from the drier areas of south-eastern and central Australia, the Tesselated Gecko attains a maximum length of only 7 centimetres. It is a nocturnal lizard, remaining concealed within a burrow in the sandy soil during daylight hours, and venturing forth after dark to prey upon the small insects that constitute the basis of its diet.

Stone Gecko *Diplodactylus vittatus*   Plate 12

The Stone Gecko is found throughout most of south-eastern Australia, with the exception of Tasmania. It shelters on the ground beneath stones and logs, or in a burrow in sandy regions. In certain areas it is erroneously believed to be capable of inflicting a venomous bite. As well as being completely inoffensive, it is of course non-venomous, as are all Australian lizards.

This common gecko grows to over 7 centimetres in length and feeds upon small soft-bodied insects.

Soft-spined Gecko *Diplodactylus williamsi* Plate 13

The Soft-spined Gecko occurs from north-western Queensland to the hinterland of northern New South Wales. An unusual feature which it shares with a few close relatives is its ability to exude a sticky, toxic substance from pores on the tail. This defensive measure apparently acts as a repellent to an aggressor.

This inoffensive lizard is relatively common in its habitat where it shelters beneath the loose bark of trees. It reaches a maximum length of 10 centimetres.

House Gecko *Gehyra australis* Plate 14

As the name suggests, this gecko frequents houses and other man-made structures where it feeds on the insects attracted by the lights after dark. It moves over the smooth surfaces of the walls and ceilings in pursuit of its quarry with the aid of specialised pads on all four feet.

The House Gecko occurs from northern Australia to western New South Wales, and in its natural state shelters beneath the bark of trees or amongst dead timber. An average length would be 10 centimetres, but larger specimens are often encountered.

Pilbara Spotted Dtella *Gehyra fenestra* Plate 15

The Pilbara Spotted Dtella is restricted to the Pilbara region of north-western Australia; however a number of geckos, similar in appearance and habits, occur throughout the northern half of Australia.

It is common in its habitat, where it shelters beneath exfoliating rock. Length: 9 centimetres.

Arnhem Land Spotted Dtella *Gehyra pamela*   Plate 16

This diminutive gecko, fully grown at 9 centimetres, is confined to the Arnhem Land region of the Northern Territory.

It is commonly encountered at night amongst the precipitous rock formations of the Arnhem Land escarpment, where it hides by day in crevices.

Dtella *Gehyra variegata*   Plate 17

This common gecko is widely distributed throughout most parts of Australia. It abounds under the loose bark of trees and beneath fallen logs, and it is not unusual for it to inhabit houses, the specialised pads on the feet enabling it to pursue flies, moths and other insects over the smooth surface of walls and ceilings. The Dtella grows to a maximum length of 10 centimetres.

Asian House Gecko *Hemidactylus frenatus*   Plate 18

The wide distribution of this gecko, from south-east Asia to the Pacific islands, is probably explained by its preference for living amongst man-made structures. In Australia it occurs in the Top End of the Northern Territory, where it has established itself in appreciable numbers during the past two decades. It is now the common House Gecko in this area, and has almost completely replaced the native House Gecko (*Gehyra australis*) which in the past has had no competition in this particular environment. The Asian House Gecko also occurs in coastal settlements of north Queensland.

It is an agile gecko which can move with little difficulty over the walls and ceilings in pursuit of insects. It is capable of varying the intensity of its colouration to such an extent that when observed after dark it appears to lack any pigmentation whatsoever. The Asian House Gecko can be considered fully grown at a length of 10 centimetres. It is the most vocal of Australia's lizards; its shrill nocturnal call is a feature of urban life in the Top End of the Northern Territory.

Prickly Gecko *Heteronotia binoei* Plate 19

This extremely common gecko can be found on the ground beneath rocks, logs and debris throughout wooded areas of Australia generally, with the exception of south-eastern and south-western districts. The colouration is variable, ranging from dull brown with lighter speckles to the brightly banded forms which are occasionally encountered. The Prickly Gecko grows to 10 centimetres in length and feeds upon small soft-bodied insects.

Desert Cave Gecko *Heteronotia spelea* Plate 20

The Desert Cave Gecko ranges from north-western Australia to the Alice Springs district of southern Northern Territory, and is also recorded from Arnhem Land and Groote Eylandt. It shelters by day in caves and crevices amongst rocky hills, and hunts by night in the vicinity of the cave entrance for insects which form the basis of its diet.

The Desert Cave Gecko grows to a length of 10 centimetres.

Beaded Gecko *Lucasium damaeum* Plate 21

This relatively common gecko occurs throughout the arid regions of central Australia and surrounding areas, where it spends the daylight hours concealed within a burrow in the red soil. It is an agile gecko, surprisingly swift in retiring from view amongst low scrub when disturbed during its nocturnal wanderings. The Beaded Gecko grows to only 10 centimetres in length and subsists upon a diet of small insects.

Spiny Knob-tailed Gecko *Nephrurus asper* Plate 22

The distinctive Spiny Knob-tailed Gecko occurs in dry, rocky areas of northern and central Australia. It is a large, ponderous gecko with bulky head and body.

When threatened it stands erect on its elongated limbs and, while raising and lowering its body, emits a rasping sound from its gaping mouth. It shelters by day in a burrow beneath rock or fallen timber.

The Spiny Knob-tailed Gecko is amongst Australia's largest geckos, considering its abbreviated tail and overall length of 15 centimetres.

Central Knob-tailed Gecko *Nephrurus levis levis*   Plate 23

The Central Knob-tailed Gecko inhabits the sandy plains of the central regions where it lives in a burrow it has excavated for itself or in a disused rabbit warren. It is nocturnal, as are all Australian geckos, vacating its burrow after sunset to prey upon smaller geckos and insects. It is one of our larger geckos, reaching a length of about 12 centimetres, and is surprisingly aggressive when provoked.

Pilbara Knob-tailed Gecko *Nephrurus levis pilbarensis*   Plate 24

This beautifully marked gecko can be distinguished from the Central Knob-tailed Gecko (*Nephrurus levis levis*) by its larger, flatter tail and its limited distribution. It is found only in the Pilbara district of north-western Australia. It reaches a length of 15 centimetres and, like its close relative, dwells in a burrow in flat, sandy areas.

Southern Knob-tailed Gecko *Nephrurus stellatus*   Plate 25

The Southern Knob-tailed Gecko is found from Eyre Peninsula in South Australia across the Nullarbor Plain to south-western Australia where a specimen has been collected near Southern Cross. It is smaller than the Central Knob-tailed Gecko (*Nephrurus levis levis*), its maximum length being 9 centimetres, but in habits it is very similar. Its distinctive spotted dorsal patterning and more diminutive tail are the most apparent features by which identification can be determined.

Castelnaui's Gecko *Oedura castelnaui*   Plate 26

Castelnaui's Gecko is closely allied to the much more widespread Velvet Gecko (*Oedura marmorata*). Unlike its near relative, it is confined in its distribution to north-eastern Queensland where it is generally found beneath the loose bark of trees. It reaches a maximum length of 15 centimetres and feeds upon insects and smaller geckos.

Cogger's Velvet Gecko *Oedura coggeri*   Plate 27

Cogger's Velvet Gecko occurs in north-eastern Queensland and is closely related to Tryon's Gecko (*Oedura tryoni*), which is found farther to the south. It lives in small groups in the crevices amongst rock outcrops, and like its southern counterpart will also be found beneath the loose bark of trees. A length of about 12 centimetres could be considered as maximum.

Jewelled Velvet Gecko *Oedura gemmata*   Plate 28

The brilliantly coloured Jewelled Velvet Gecko is confined in its distribution to the Arnhem Land escarpment of the Northern Territory. It shelters by day in crevices amongst cliffs and outlying rock outcrops and forages at night on the rock face. The Jewelled Velvet Gecko reaches a maximum length of 14 centimetres.

Lesueur's Gecko *Oedura lesueurii*   Plate 29

This small, common gecko occurs from south-eastern New South Wales to north-eastern Queensland, where it is found sheltering beneath stones, in rock crevices, and under the loose bark of trees. It feeds on small insects and grows to a length of 10 centimetres. Like all geckos it has the ability to cast off its tail when molested. The violent contractions of the dismembered portion are meant to draw the attention of the predator, enabling the lizard to make its escape. A new, though imperfect tail will grow within a short length of time.

Velvet Gecko *Oedura marmorata*   Plate 30

Growing to a maximum length of 15 centimetres, the Velvet Gecko is widely distributed throughout northern and central Australia. It is generally discovered beneath the loose bark of trees, but will also be found in crevices and beneath stones. It is nocturnal in habit, and feeds upon smaller geckos and insects.

Although juvenile Velvet Geckos are brightly banded, these markings generally become less distinct with age.

Blotched Gecko *Oedura monilis*   Plate 31

This handsomely marked gecko occurs throughout the hinterland of south-eastern Queensland and north-eastern New South Wales, where it lives under the loose bark of trees, or beneath large rocks.

The Blotched Gecko reaches a length of about 12 centimetres and is insectivorous.

Zig-zag Gecko *Oedura rhombifer*   Plate 32

The Zig-zag Gecko is distributed throughout coastal northern Australia and the adjacent hinterland.

It grows to approximately 10 centimetres in length and is commonly encountered behind the loose bark of trees and beneath ground debris.

Robust Gecko *Oedura robusta*   Plate 33

A large gecko reaching a maximum length of 15 centimetres, the Robust Gecko occurs from north-eastern Queensland to north-eastern New South Wales. It dwells within the hollows and crevices of dead trees, beneath loose bark and also in rock crevices.

The Robust Gecko will not hesitate to discard its tail if seized by an enemy, and although it is capable of regeneration, the new tail will lack the perfect proportion and markings of the original.

Tryon's Gecko *Oedura tryoni*   Plate 34

This beautifully marked gecko occurs from north-eastern New South Wales to south-eastern Queensland. It is a gregarious species,

17

generally living in small colonies or family groups beneath exfoliated granite sheets, in rock crevices or under the loose bark of trees.

Unlike their parents, the juveniles are dull brown in colour with faint, yellow spots. Tryon's Gecko grows to a maximum length of 15 centimetres and emerges after sunset to feed upon a variety of small insects.

Marbled Gecko *Phyllodactylus marmoratus* Plate 35

This common gecko occurs throughout a large area of southern Australia where it abounds beneath the loose bark of trees, in rock crevices, and occasionally amongst ground debris.

The Marbled Gecko reaches a maximum length of 11 centimetres and feeds upon small soft-bodied insects.

Leaf-tailed Gecko *Phyllurus cornutus* Plate 36

As it may attain a length of 25 centimetres, the Leaf-tailed Gecko is considered to be the largest gecko in Australia. It is an inhabitant of coastal rainforests from northern New South Wales to far north-eastern Queensland. Arboreal in its habits, it shelters beneath the loose bark of trees during the daylight hours, and emerges after dark to prey upon insects, which form the basis of its diet.

The Leaf-tailed Gecko will readily discard its tail when seized by an enemy. It is somewhat unusual for a mature specimen to possess an original tail, which, unlike the regenerated tail, is adorned with spikes.

Broad-tailed Rock Gecko *Phyllurus platurus* Plate 37

The Broad-tailed Rock Gecko occurs in coastal New South Wales where it conceals itself deep within rock crevices during the daylight hours.

This large gecko reaches a maximum length of 15 centimetres and is occasionally found in suburban houses. When seized by an enemy it invariably utters a prolonged "squeal" while twisting the body and tail vigorously in an attempt to break free.

It is oviparous, the female laying two eggs which are usually deposited in the furthermost recesses of the crevice in which it shelters.

Giant Cave Gecko *Pseudothecadactylus lindneri*   **Plate 38**

The Giant Cave Gecko is one of the largest and most pugnacious of Australia's geckos, but was until recently unknown to science. That it could pass unnoticed is perhaps explained by prior isolation of its habitat: this 18 centimetre long gecko is restricted to the rugged escarpment country of Arnhem Land, Northern Territory and the Kimberley Ranges of Western Australia.

It is an inhabitant of caves and crevices, and ventures from its retreat at night to forage on the cliffs and in small trees nearby for insects and spiders. With its pseudo-adhesive digital pads and a corresponding pad on the undersurface of the tail tip, it is able to scale a perpendicular rock face with ease.

Beaked Gecko *Rhynchoedura ornata*   **Plate 39**

This small lizard may be considered full grown at a length of 7 centimetres. It has an extensive distribution throughout the desert and semidesert areas of all States of the mainland.

The Beaked Gecko shelters within a burrow, in earth cracks or under rocks during the daylight hours, emerging after dark to feed upon small soft-bodied insects.

Thick-tailed Gecko *Underwoodisaurus milii*   **Plate 40**

One of the largest and most brightly coloured of the Australian geckos, the Thick-tailed Gecko occurs throughout the southern half of Australia. It is a surprisingly aggressive gecko, capable of emitting a short "coughing" sound when molested. It grows to over 15 centimetres in length and is usually found beneath a large rock, though specimens from inland areas frequent ground burrows.

LEGLESS LIZARDS
Pygopodidae

Delma inornata   Plate 41

This shy legless lizard measures approximately 38 centimetres in length and is an inhabitant of south-eastern Australia.

It occurs in a wide range of habitats, from coastal forests to arid grassland in the western extremities of its range, and shelters amongst grass tussocks or beneath fallen timber.

Sharp-snouted Legless Lizard *Delma nasuta*   Plate 42

The Sharp-snouted Legless Lizard occurs in dry, porcupine grass-dominated environs of Western Australia, South Australia and the central regions.

It is an active, nocturnal lizard which shelters amongst the spiky porcupine grass by day. When disturbed, it appears over-zealous in its efforts to escape, for it will sometimes leap up to 15 centimetres from the ground while progressing rapidly in the direction of the nearest shelter. This "jumping" behaviour may well be allied to its defence, since it will repeat this frantic leaping on one spot if the avenue of escape is blocked.

The Sharp-snouted Legless Lizard reaches a maximum length of 30 centimetres, and is erroneously known as "spinifex snake" throughout much of its range.

Delma tincta   Plate 43

This swift-moving legless lizard is widely distributed throughout northern Australia.

It shelters beneath fallen timber and rocks and grows to a total length of 28 centimetres.

Burton's Legless Lizard *Lialis burtonis*   Plates 44A, 44B

This relatively common lizard is distributed throughout Australia, with the exception of Tasmania. In colouration and markings it is highly variable, though it may be immediately recognised by its long, pointed snout. The habitat of this widely distributed lizard is perhaps as variable as its colouration, for it is as much at home in desert areas as it is in coastal forests.

Burton's Legless Lizard feeds principally upon small lizards, and may attain a length of over 60 centimetres. Although diurnal in its habits in the southern regions, it is most active at night in inland areas and the far north.

Common Scaly Foot *Pygopus lepidopodus*   Plate 45

Although similar in appearance to a snake, the Common Scaly Foot may be distinguished by its broad fleshy tongue, which is protruded regularly in order to clean the transparent scale covering the eye. It shelters beneath rock or fallen timber, and is present throughout southern Australia, with the exception of Tasmania and the desert regions.

This shy lizard retires swiftly from view when disturbed in any way, its mode of progression being snake-like. It grows to over 60 centimetres in length and feeds upon insects and occasionally small skinks.

Black-headed Scaly Foot *Pygopus nigriceps*   Plate 46

Owing to the apparent absence of limbs, the Black-headed Scaly Foot is often mistaken for a snake. It is relatively common throughout the drier areas of Australia but is rarely observed, owing to its nocturnal habits.

Although it may grow to a length of 60 centimetres, specimens of this size are uncommon, since the long tail is highly prone to dismemberment, and the subsequent regenerated section is shorter than the original.

21

The more intense colouration and head markings of the juvenile usually fade considerably with age. This lizard is completely harmless, but it can effectively mimic the striking stance and actions of a venomous snake in an endeavour to intimidate an aggressor.

DRAGONS
Agamidae

Mountain Dragon *Amphibolurus diemensis*　　　　Plate 47

Reaching a maximum length of 20 centimetres, the Mountain Dragon occurs in Tasmania, Victoria and on the New South Wales coast as far north as the Sydney region. It is usually found on or near the ground, and is often encountered in pairs, the male being distinguished by its brighter markings. Owing to its small size, its diet is restricted to small insects.

Although occasionally mistaken for the young of the Jacky Lizard (*Amphibolurus muricatus*), it may be immediately distinguished by the blue colouring of the interior of the mouth.

Jacky Lizard *Amphibolurus muricatus*　　　　Plate 48

A common lizard, widely distributed along the eastern and southern coast of Australia, the Jacky Lizard may attain a maximum length of 42 centimetres.

It will readily climb trees, though it is normally encountered on the ground, where it adopts a bipedal gait over short distances when disturbed. If cornered, the Jacky Lizard will assume a threatening pose, with mouth agape, displaying the bright yellow colouring of the interior. It is aggressive in its feeding habits, preying upon worms, small skinks, and insects.

Nobbi *Amphibolurus nobbi* Plate 49

The Nobbi is an inhabitant of dry forest areas of eastern Australia. It perches atop tree stumps, fence posts or amongst low shrubs, and descends swiftly to the ground to seize passing insects.

This alert dragon grows to a length of 23 centimetres.

Chameleon Dragon *Chelosania brunnea* Plate 50

While most Australian Agamids are alert, swift-moving lizards, the slow-moving Chameleon Dragon is a notable exception. This sedentary lizard inhabits open forest in the Kimberley district of Western Australia and the Top End of the Northern Territory. It is not particularly common in its habitat, where it is generally encountered amongst shrubs and fallen timber.

The Chameleon Dragon is fully grown at a length of 23 centimetres.

Frilled Lizard *Chlamydosaurus kingii* Plate 51

Widely distributed throughout the well-wooded areas of the northern half of Australia, the Frilled Lizard in undoubtedly our most spectacular reptile. Whereas the Queensland specimens are grey in colour, the Northern Territory and Western Australian varieties are brick-red with fiery orange and yellow on the "frill".

Although normally encountered on the ground, the Frilled Lizard is quick to scurry to the safety of a tree when danger threatens. If intercepted before being able to do so, it will turn to face its aggressor with "frill" erected and mouth agape. During its efforts to intimidate its tormentor it may stand on its hind legs, rocking from side to side while emitting a loud and prolonged hiss.

The Frilled Lizard, which reaches a length of almost 90 centimetres, feeds upon insects and mice.

Ring-tailed Dragon *Ctenophorus caudicinctus* Plate 52

The Ring-tailed Dragon occurs from western Queensland, throughout the Northern Territory to north-western Australia. The distinctive markings and bright colouring are less obvious on the female of this species, which is also smaller in stature. It is common in rocky areas of the north-west, where it is usually observed perched high on a rock, under which it will retreat when disturbed. A mature male may reach a length of 28 centimetres.

Tawny Dragon *Ctenophorus decresii* Plate 53

The Tawny Dragon is a swift-moving lizard, occurring in rocky districts from south-eastern South Australia to far-western New South Wales. Unlike the brightly coloured male, the female of this species is a rather dull brown in colour.

The Tawny Dragon feeds upon a variety of small insects, including grasshoppers, moths and beetles, and grows to a maximum length of 25 centimetres.

Peninsula Dragon *Ctenophorus fionni* Plate 54

The Peninsula Dragon is an inhabitant of the Eyre Peninsula and adjacent islands of South Australia. It is a rock dweller, similar in appearance and habits to the Tawny Dragon (*Ctenophorus decresii*) with which is has been often confused.

The Peninsula Dragon exhibits considerable colour diversity within its limited range, and there is also marked variation between the brightly coloured males and more sombre females.

A fully grown Peninsula Dragon measures 28 centimetres in length.

Netted Dragon *Ctenophorus nuchalis* Plate 55

This large-headed dragon occurs in dry inland areas of all States, excluding Victoria and Tasmania. It is common in central Australia, where it is usually observed perched on a fence post or termite mound. When danger threatens it is quick to scurry to the safety of its burrow, which is generally close by.

The Netted Dragon grows to over 30 centimetres in length and feeds upon termites and other insects.

Ornate Dragon *Ctenophorus ornatus*   Plate 56

An agile, sun-loving lizard, the Ornate Dragon inhabits granite outcrops in south-western Australia. When alarmed, this swift-moving lizard will retire to the comparative safety of a rock crevice or beneath a large granite slab. It reaches a maximum length of 25 centimetres and feeds on a variety of insects.

The Ornate Dragon is oviparous, the female depositing from two to five eggs in soft soil on the fringe of the outcrop.

Painted Dragon *Ctenophorus pictus*   Plate 57

During the mating season the male Painted Dragon is undoubtedly our most brightly coloured lizard. The female is slightly smaller than the male, which reaches a maximum length of 25 centimetres, and is normally rusty brown in colour. The pair dwell in a shallow burrow which is usually located at the base of saltbush or other low scrub. This extremely active dragon is found in dry, sandy areas of the southern half of Australia, away from the coast, and feeds on a large variety of small insects.

The male Painted Dragon has the ability to raise its dorsal crest when agitated.

Boyd's Forest Dragon *Gonocephalus boydii*   Plate 58

An uncommon lizard, living deep in the rainforests of north-eastern Queensland, Boyd's Forest Dragon is among our most spectacular reptiles. It is slow-moving and inoffensive, relying largely upon camouflage for protection. This colourful dragon grows to a length of 50 centimetres and feeds upon insects, worms, and mice.

Rainforest Dragon *Gonocephalus spinipes*   Plate 59

An inhabitant of the coastal rainforests of northern New South Wales and southern Queensland, the Rainforest Dragon reaches a maximum length of 35 centimetres. Owing to its highly efficient camouflage, and the inaccessibility of the rainforest, the Rainforest

Dragon is rarely observed in its habitat.

It is in general an inoffensive lizard, but may resort to an aggressive display if provoked. It is capable of a two-legged gait, but is relatively slow and clumsy in comparison to the majority of dragons in this respect.

This uncommon dragon feeds upon insects, worms, and small mice.

Gilbert's Dragon *Lophognathus gilberti*   Plate 60

An extremely agile arboreal lizard, Gilbert's Dragon is distributed throughout northern Australia generally, where it is often encountered in the trees bordering rivers and billabongs.

Colouring varies greatly between specimens from different localities, the southern form usually being a shade of grey or brown and less conspicuous than its northern counterpart, the male of which may have a black throat and a snow-white streak on the side of the head. It is frequently observed in pairs, the female being distinguished by its sombre colouring and smaller stature. The head is rather slender and the long tail is almost three times the length of the head and body. Surprisingly aggressive when captured, Gilbert's Dragon will struggle vigorously, repeatedly trying to bite its tormentor. It is known to exceed a length of 50 centimetres.

Long-nosed Water Dragon *Lophognathus longirostris*   Plate 61

An agile, aboreal lizard, reaching a maximum length of 45 centimetres, the Long-nosed Water Dragon occurs from the central regions of the continent to the Western Australian coast. It is usually found in the trees bordering rivers and creeks and will readily enter the water when disturbed. It is similar in appearance to Gilbert's Dragon (*Lophognathus gilberti*), though even more slender, and the tail is over three times the length of the head and body. The Long-nosed Water Dragon feeds almost entirely upon insects.

Northern Water Dragon *Lophognathus temporalis*   Plate 62

This arboreal lizard is found in the mangrove swamps and trees bordering coastal waterways from north-western Australia to Cape York Peninsula. In the Northern Territory it is most often found amongst pandanus bush, taking full advantage of the spiky top section of this plant when seeking shelter. It feeds upon a large variety of insects, which it has little difficulty in capturing, owing to its speed and climbing ability.

The male may reach a length of 60 centimetres, and is larger, more robust and more brightly coloured than the female.

Thorny Devil *Moloch horridus*   Plate 63

This unique lizard differs so greatly from all other Australian species that no mistake can possibly be made with its identification. It is slow-moving and completely inoffensive by nature, apparently relying upon its grotesque appearance to ward off predators.

The Thorny Devil lives entirely upon a diet of small black ants, and may devour over a thousand during the course of one meal. It is an egg-layer, the female depositing up to eight eggs at the base of a burrow which she has scooped in the soft red sand.

This spectacular lizard inhabits the desert and semidesert areas of central and Western Australia, and reaches a maximum length of 20 centimetres.

Eastern Water Dragon *Physignathus lesueurii lesueurii*   Plate 64

A large semiaquatic lizard, the Eastern Water Dragon occurs along rivers and creeks of the eastern coast, from Cape York Peninsula to southern New South Wales. It is one of the few lizards having external differences that make it easy to distinguish between the sexes. Mature males are more robust, the nuchal crest is more pronounced and the chest is blood-red. Male Water Dragons grow larger than females, specimens over 90 centimetres being recorded.

27

The Eastern Water Dragon is a shy lizard, often observed on a tree limb overhanging the water, where it will drop in without the slightest hesitation when disturbed.

Gippsland Water Dragon *Physignathus lesueurii howittii*
Plate 65

This impressive lizard inhabits coastal watercourses from Gippsland in Victoria north to the Nowra district of New South Wales. At its northernmost limit it is sympatric with the Eastern Water Dragon (*Physignathus lesueurii lesueurii*), but may be immediately distinguished by its deep blue-green colour. Its habits are identical to those of the Eastern Water Dragon, and it is rarely found at any distance from the water.

The Gippsland Water Dragon follows a complicated pattern of social behaviour. Each mature male, distinguished by its large size, striking colour and pronounced nuchal crest, is in control of a section of the river bank and a number of the smaller females. The size of the area and the number of females under his control seem to be governed by the size and strength of the male dragon, which may attain a length of about 1 metre. Immature males, and males too old to maintain a "harem" are forced to lead a solitary existence.

The Gippsland Water Dragon feeds upon almost any live food small enough for it to overpower.

Western Bearded Dragon *Pogona minima*
Plate 66

The Western Bearded Dragon attains a maximum length of 35 centimetres. It is less robust and the spines are underdeveloped in comparison to those of the Inland Bearded Dragon (*Pogona vitticeps*).

The habits of this rather sedentary reptile are very similar to those of its eastern relatives. It is most often observed perched on a tree stump or fence post, venturing to the ground only when attracted by the movement of a small skink or insect.

Inland Bearded Dragon *Pogona vitticeps*
Plate 67

The Inland Bearded Dargon ranges throughout western Queensland

and New South Wales to South Australia and southern Northern Territory. It is a common lizard, often observed in country areas basking in the sun on a fence post or tree stump. It relies principally on camouflage for its protection, but if this fails it will resort to a spectacular defensive stance. The mouth is opened fully displaying the bright-yellow interior, the "beard" is extended and the body takes on an enlarged appearance owing to an expansion of the ribs. Specimens from central Australia are often reddish in colour.

The Inland Bearded Dragon attains a maximum length of 65 centimetres. It is very partial to live food, to which it is attracted by the slightest movement, devouring a variety of insects, worms, mice, and small lizards. It will also feed upon ground herbage, showing a particular liking for dandelion blossoms.

Earless Dragon *Tympanocryptis cephalus*   Plate 68

As the common name would suggest, an Earless Dragon is easily recognisable by its lack of visible ear openings. There are a number of different varieties inhabiting the drier regions of Australia, none of them exceeding 15 centimetres in length. In flat areas an interesting habit of this lizard is to position itself vertically, resting on its hind limbs and tail, with the front limbs held firmly on its sides. It can remain motionless in this state for a considerable length of time, apparently in an effort to afford itself a better view of the surrounding countryside. When disturbed, it will seek shelter within a burrow, which is normally located at the base of low scrub or beneath a rock.

MONITORS
Varanidae

Spiny-tailed Monitor *Varanus acanthurus*   Plates 69A, 69B

As much at home on the open plains of the Barkly Tablelands as it is in rocky mountainous areas, the Spiny-tailed Monitor occurs from north-western Australia through the Northern Territory to the Mount Isa district of Queensland.

This handsomely marked lizard reaches a maximum length of about 65 centimetres and feeds on small lizards, insects, and mice.

Short-tailed Monitor *Varanus brevicauda* Plate 70

This tiny monitor has the distinction of being the world's smallest, attaining a length of only 20 centimetres. Owing to the remoteness of the area in which it occurs, and the desolate nature of the environment, few specimens have been collected to be studied in detail. It is found in open sandy country from north-western Australia to the Queensland–Northern Territory border, where the most prominent feature of the landscape is porcupine grass. It shelters in a shallow burrow concealed amongst the grass, and feeds upon insects and small lizards.

During September or October the Short-tailed Monitor deposits two or three eggs beneath the red soil, and approximately nine weeks later the young hatch, measuring an incredible 8 centimetres in overall length.

Stripe-tailed Monitor *Varanus caudolineatus* Plate 71

The Stripe-tailed Monitor can easily be confused with Gillen's Pigmy Monitor (*Varanus gilleni*), for they are both very similar in appearance as well as in habits. It has a more limited distribution, being confined to Western Australia where it occurs from Port Hedland in the north to within 195 kilometres of Perth and as far west as the Kalgoorlie district. The loose bark and crevices of the mulga tree provide the usual form of shelter for this arboreal goanna, but it has also been found beneath exfoliated granite. It reaches a maximum length of 28 centimetres and feeds upon insects and small lizards.

Desert Pygmy Monitor *Varanus eremius* Plate 72

Like many inhabitants of Australia's arid centre, the Desert Pygmy

Monitor is closely associated with the porcupine grass which dominates the desert landscape. Its spiky recesses provide both sanctuary and an abundant source of insects for food.

The Desert Pygmy Monitor reaches a total length of 40 centimetres and inhabits the sandy desert plains of central and Western Australia.

Perenty *Varanus giganteus* Plate 73

The Perenty, Australia's largest lizard, occasionally attains a length of 2½ metres. It is a shy species distributed throughout sandy, mountainous areas of central and Western Australia, where it lives in a secluded burrow amongst rocky hills.

During the early hours of the morning the Perenty ventures from its burrow into open country where it preys upon smaller lizards, mammals, and birds. Owing to its extreme shyness, it is rarely observed in its habitat. At the first sign of danger it will lie flat on the ground, remaining motionless until the danger passes.

Gillen's Pigmy Monitor *Varanus gilleni* Plate 74

An arboreal lizard from the central Australian region, Gillen's Pigmy Monitor rarely exceeds a length of 35 centimetres. During the heat of the day it shelters in the hollows of a dead tree, venturing forth at dusk to prey upon the geckos and cockroaches and other insects that live beneath the loose bark. This secretive monitor remains beneath the bark overnight, to resume hunting during the cooler hours of the morning. It returns to the tree hollow as the sun regains its full strength.

Glauert's Monitor *Varanus glauerti* Plate 75

Apparently confined to the Kimberley Ranges of north-western Australia, Glauert's Monitor is a shy, rock-dwelling lizard which retreats to the safety of a crevice when approached.

It feeds on insects and small lizards. A fully grown monitor may measure 80 centimetres in length.

Black-palmed Rock Monitor *Varanus glebopalma* Plate 76

This shy monitor inhabits scattered rocky environs, from the Kimberley Ranges of north-western Australia through the Top End of the Northern Territory to the Mount Isa district of north-western Queensland.

It is a common lizard amongst the precipitous rock formations of the Arnhem Land escarpment, and is most active during the cooler hours of early morning and at sundown. When disturbed it quickly retires to the safety of a rock crevice.

An adult lizard may measure 1 metre, but much of this length is contained in its exceptionally long tail. The small black pads arranged on the soles of the feet assist this active lizard to negotiate its rocky habitat.

Gould's Monitor *Varanus gouldii gouldii* Plate 77

Found throughout Australia in almost any habitat from desert to rain-forest, Gould's Monitor is undoubtedly the most widespread of the Australian monitors. The colouration varies to a large degree between specimens from different localities, the eastern coastal variety being dark and inconspicuously marked in comparison to the brightly coloured specimens from inland areas.

When disturbed, it can display an amazing burst of speed, usually to disappear into a burrow or disused rabbit warren. Growing to a length of over 1½ metres, Gould's Monitor is one of the largest lizards in Australia. It is a voracious feeder, known to devour snakes, lizards, rats, mice, rabbits, birds, and also carrion.

Central Sand Monitor *Varanus gouldii flavirufus* Plate 78

Restricted in its distribution to the central Australian region, the Central Sand Monitor differs from the common Gould's Monitor (*Varanus gouldii gouldii*) in colouration and maximum length. It is perhaps the most brightly coloured of the Australian monitors and may be considered outsize at a length of 1 metre.

It excavates a shallow burrow in the soft red sand, the end being very close to the surface. If an attempt is made to remove the lizard from the burrow it will break through the surface some distance from the entrance and make its escape. The Monitor feeds principally on lizards and mice.

Mangrove Monitor *Varanus indicus*   **Plate 79**

This large semiaquatic monitor lives amongst the mangroves of the tidal rivers and creeks of Cape York Peninsula and Arnhem Land in the far north of Australia. It is also to be found in the East Indies, New Guinea, and on a number of islands in the Pacific. The Mangrove Monitor attains a maximum length of almost 2 metres, and its food consists of fish, crustaceans, mammals, and juvenile crocodiles. It is somewhat crocodilian in habit, moving from the bank to the safety of the water when alarmed.

King's Monitor *Varanus kingorum*   **Plate 80**

King's Monitor is a small rock-dwelling monitor recently discovered in, and apparently confined to, the Kimberley Ranges of northwestern Australia and the adjacent area of the Northern Territory.

It lives in the crevices of exfoliating sandstone and grows to a length of approximately 25 centimetres.

Merten's Water Monitor *Varanus mertensi*   **Plate 81**

Expertly adapted to a semiaquatic existence, Merten's Water Monitor is as much at home in the water as it is on land. It is a powerful, somewhat solid monitor, occurring among the permanent waterways of central Queensland, coastal Northern Territory, and the Kimberley region in Western Australia.

This handsome monitor subsists upon a diet of crustaceans, fish, large water insects, frogs, lizards, and mammals. Most of its food is secured beneath the water; it walks the river bottom with eyes open in much the same manner as other monitors do on land. It is capable of remarkable speed beneath the water when alarmed. With limbs pressed firmly to its sides, it uses the powerful vertically compressed tail to propel it swiftly through the water with speed and agility equal to that of a crocodile.

There is a record of a clutch of nine eggs which were laid in a carefully constructed burrow with a chamber at the end. A quantity of leaf mould was deposited with the eggs by the female, and the entrance was sealed firmly.

Merten's Water Monitor reaches a length of 1¼ metres.

Mitchell's Water Monitor *Varanus mitchelli*   Plate 82

A shy semiaquatic species, Mitchell's Water Monitor occurs on the permanent waterways of coastal Northern Territory and north-western Australia. Its favourite haunt is a pandanus limb overhanging the water, into which it will drop with little hesitation when danger threatens.

Mitchell's Water Monitor feeds on fish, frogs, crustaceans, insects, small lizards, and mice, and may reach a total length of 60 centimetres. It is a proficient swimmer, spending a large amount of the day in the water and retiring to a hollow pandanus limb at dusk.

Varanus panoptes   Plate 83

This large monitor may exceed a length of 1½ metres. It is similar in appearance to the more widely distributed Gould's Monitor (*Varanus gouldii gouldii*) but is confined in its distribution to north-western Australia and the Top End of the Northern Territory.

An adult monitor is reluctant to retreat when approached. It raises its forebody and, while balancing on its hind limbs and tail, rocks slowly from side to side, hissing violently and hurtling out its bifid tongue in defiance. As well as for defence, the "tripod" stance is employed to afford a better view of an approaching object, or, in the shade of a tree, to keep the body temperature down during the hotter hours of midday.

Green Tree Monitor *Varanus prasinus*   Plate 84

Common throughout the island of New Guinea, the Green Tree Monitor has also been reported recently from the top of Cape York

Peninsula, Queensland, a region where other members of typical New Guinea fauna are represented

It is a forest-dweller, largely arboreal, but also descending to the ground to feed. This brilliantly coloured monitor attains an overall length of 80 centimetres.

Ridge-tailed Monitor *Varanus primordius*   Plate 85

This rare monitor is confined in its distribution to the Top End of the Northern Territory, where it occurs among rocky outcrops in timbered areas. Very little has been recorded of its habits, since only a few specimens have been collected to date. It is similar in appearance to the much more common Storr's Monitor (*Varanus storri*), with which it has been confused in the past.

The Ridge-tailed Monitor is a shy lizard which feeds upon insects and small lizards. It can be considered full-grown at a length of 30 centimetres.

Rusty Monitor *Varanus semiremex*   Plate 86

An inhabitant of Queensland's eastern coast, the Rusty Monitor grows to over 75 centimetres in length. It makes its home in the hollow limb of a tree. Although not a true water monitor, it is most often encountered near the water or in coastal mangrove swamps, and when alarmed it will readily enter the water.

In its feeding habits it shows a particular liking for small crabs, but will also devour frogs, insects, mice, and lizards.

Spencer's Monitor *Varanus spenceri*   Plates 87A, 87B

Growing to almost 1¼ metres in length, Spencer's Monitor occurs in black-soil areas of Queensland and the Northern Territory, where it shelters in a hole or deep crack in the earth. This relatively placid monitor is often encountered on the Barkly Highway in the vicinity of the Northern Territory and Queensland border, where the surrounding area is extremely flat and devoid of trees. It is heavy-set and does not hesitate to use its short, thick tail as a defensive weapon.

Spencer's Monitor is carnivorous, as are all monitors, feeding on rats, mice, and lizards.

There is a record of fourteen eggs being produced by this lizard. The young measure approximately 22 centimetres in length on hatching, and they are strongly banded with yellow and chocolate brown.

Storr's Monitor *Varanus storri* Plate 88

This small spiny-tailed monitor occurs in scattered localities throughout inland Queensland to the Kimberley Ranges of Western Australia, and abounds amongst rocks in dry, open country.

Although a length of over 40 centimetres has been recorded, Storr's Monitor rarely exceeds a total length of 30 centimetres. It is largely insectivorous in its feeding habits, but will also devour lizards and small mice. Juveniles are approximately 8 centimetres in length on hatching and are far more colourful than an adult, which may have little if any markings at all.

Spotted Tree Monitor *Varanus timorensis similis* Plate 89

An arboreal lizard, making its home in a hollow tree limb, the Spotted Tree Monitor is widely distributed throughout northern Australia. The most common colouration is grey-brown with light speckles forming obscure ocellations; however, specimens from different localities are often greatly diverse in colour and markings. The far north-eastern coastal variety is darker, with ocellations in the form of distinct rings grouped into irregular cross-bands. The central Queensland phase is pale grey with darker reticulations, and sometimes tinged with rusty red. Length: 60 centimetres.

The Spotted Tree Monitor ventures from its arboreal abode to the ground to prey on mice, lizards, frogs, and insects.

Black-headed Monitor *Varanus tristis tristis*   Plate 90

This slender monitor enjoys a wide distribution throughout Western
and central Australia, where it lives in a hollow tree limb, rock crevice
or burrow. It is an extremely fast-moving lizard, capable of an
amazing burst of speed when alarmed or in pursuit of its prey.

The Black-headed Monitor attains a length of 75 centimetres, and
feeds principally upon lizards, insects, and mice. The dark colouration
of the head and shoulders may or may not be present, and appears to
be more apparent among mature specimens.

Freckled Monitor *Varanus tristis orientalis*   Plate 91

The Freckled Monitor could, with some justification, be confused
with an immature Black-headed Monitor (*Varanus tristis tristis*). But
it fails to reach a length comparable with that of its close relative, and
also lacks the black head and tail markings which are characteristic of
a full-grown Black-headed Monitor.

The Freckled Monitor occurs throughout northern Australia, and
can be considered fully grown at a length of 60 centimetres. It is
generally arboreal, inhabiting a hollow tree limb, but it spends much
of the day on the ground in pursuit of the insects, mice, and small
lizards on which it preys.

Lace Monitor *Varanus varius*   Plates 92A, 92B

More commonly known by the name of Tree Goanna, the Lace
Monitor is Australia's second largest lizard, growing to a length of 2
metres. Although normally encountered on the ground, it can display
the greatest efficiency in climbing the tallest of trees when alarmed. It
is a very capable hunter, preying upon almost any bird, mammal or
reptile of suitable dimension, and it will also feed on carrion and eggs.

The Lace Monitor occurs in forested areas from the far north-
eastern coast of Queensland, through coastal and inland New South
Wales, to Victoria and South Australia. In the western regions of its
distribution there exists a colour variation marked with broad yellow
and black cross-bands.

It is oviparous, as are all monitors, producing approximately six eggs to the clutch, which are usually deposited in a termite mound. On hatching, the young are strikingly banded with yellow and black and measure approximately 28 centimetres.

SKINKS
Scincidae

Jewelled Four-fingered Skink *Carlia jarnoldae*   Plate 93

This tiny lizard reaches a maximum length of barely 9 centimetres, but what it may lack in size is certainly made up for by its brilliant colouring. It inhabits timbered areas of north-eastern Queensland where it shelters on the ground beneath rocks or fallen timber and feeds on small insects and insect larvae.

Legless Skink *Coeranoscincus frontalis*   Plate 94

An inhabitant of the Atherton Tableland rainforest in north-eastern Queensland, the Legless Skink burrows amongst the humus layer of the forest floor and shelters beneath decomposing timber.

Its polished scales, blunt tail and small, pointed head are typical adaptations for a subterranean lifestyle. The Legless Skink is entirely devoid of limbs and grows to approximately 30 centimetres in length.

Fence Skink *Cryptoblepharus virgatus*   Plate 95

This active lizard is often observed darting swiftly over walls and fences in suburban gardens on warm summer days. It occurs along the eastern coast of Australia, and in its natural state shelters beneath the loose bark of trees and occasionally under flat stones.

The Fence Skink attains a maximum length of 10 centimetres and feeds upon flies and small insects.

Ocellated Skink *Ctenotus pantherinus*   Plate 96

The Ocellated Skink occurs in flat, semidesert areas from north-western Queensland and throughout central Australia to the north-western coast. It is most active during the cooler hours of the morning or late afternoon, darting swiftly amongst porcupine grass or into a burrow when disturbed. This fast-moving skink is largely insectivorous in its feeding habits and attains a maximum length of 23 centimetres.

Striped Skink *Ctenotus robustus*   Plate 97

The Striped Skink is extensively distributed throughout much of northern and eastern Australia. It is a swift-moving diurnal skink, which takes refuge in a burrow, usually beneath rock or fallen timber. This common skink reaches a maximum length of 25 centimetres and feeds principally upon small insects.

Copper-tailed Skink *Ctenotus taeniolatus*   Plate 98

A swift-moving diurnal lizard, the Copper-tailed Skink is found in rocky coastal areas of eastern Australia. It is most often encountered sunning itself on a large, flat rock, beneath which it shelters in a burrow it has excavated. The female skink deposits up to five eggs in the sandy soil beneath the rock, and when hatched the young measure approximately 6 centimetres in length. This common lizard reaches a maximum length of 20 centimetres and feeds upon flies, worms, and a large variety of small insects.

Cunningham's Skink *Egernia cunninghami*   Plate 99

This common skink occurs in rocky mountainous areas from south-eastern Queensland through New South Wales and Victoria to South Australia. It is highly gregarious, living in large colonies within rock crevices and occasionally in hollow logs.

The colouration of this large skink varies considerably in specimens from different localities. Apart from the most common form, which is olive-brown with lighter flecks, there is a distinct variety inhabiting the Sydney sandstone district, and a strikingly marked form occurring in the New England region of north-eastern New South Wales.

Cunningham's Skink attains a maximum length of 45 centimetres, and its food consists of insects, worms, snails, and a variety of native berries and ground herbage.

Depressed Spiny Skink *Egernia depressa* — Plate 100

The Depressed Spiny Skink is restricted in its distribution to the State of Western Australia, where it occurs from the Pilbara region in the north to the Kalgoorlie district. At first glance it could be mistaken for the young of the Spiny-tailed Skink (*Egernia stokesii*), but it can be readily identified by an examination of the scales on the tail. Its larger relative has a single spine on each scale, the Depressed Spiny Skink has three.

It is a gregarious lizard, living in groups in the crevices amongst rocky outcrops, in tree hollows, and in the large termite mounds that are abundant throughout its distribution area. It reaches a maximum length of 15 centimetres and is primarily insectivorous in its feeding habits.

Major Skink *Egernia frerei* — Plate 101

This handsome skink inhabits heavily forested areas from the Tweed River in New South Wales along the entire eastern coast of Queensland. It is a swift-moving lizard, making its home in a burrow beneath a large rock or log on the forest floor.

The Major Skink attains a maximum length of 45 centimetres and subsists on a diet of insects, worms, snails, and mice.

Hosmer's Skink *Egernia hosmeri* — Plate 102

Common in its habitat, yet somewhat secretive by nature, Hosmer's Skink reaches a length of 38 centimetres. It is a gregarious lizard living in small colonies in rocky areas of the north Queensland hinterland. Owing to the strongly keeled scales on the dorsal and lateral surfaces, it is extremely difficult to remove this lizard from the rock crevices in which it shelters.

Desert Skink *Egernia inornata*   Plate 103

This large-headed skink is widely distributed throughout the desert and semidesert areas of central Australia and adjacent districts. It excavates a burrow in the sandy soil, into which it retires swiftly when disturbed. The burrow generally has a rear entrance covered with a thin crust of sand or concealed amongst porcupine grass, from which the lizard may make its escape if necessary.

The Desert Skink attains a maximum length of 18 centimetres and is primarily insectivorous in its feeding habits.

King's Skink *Egernia kingii*   Plate 104

This large skink occurs in rocky coastal areas of south-western Australia, from Esperance in the south to as far north as Dirk Hartog Island. King's Skink is common on many offshore islands, where it is usually the dominant form of the reptile population.

Its diet is highly variable: it will feed upon insects, mice, the broken eggs of seabirds, and the fruit and flowers of a variety of plants. It is a known scavenger, picking any edible object from among the seaweed drifts on the beach.

King's Skink is a robust lizard, reaching a maximum length of 56 centimetres. Specimens from northern areas tend to be smaller than their southern counterparts and may be faintly marked with spots and stripes.

This powerful skink generally gives birth to two live young, which, unlike the adults, are usually speckled with white on the dorsal and lateral surfaces.

Land Mullet *Egernia major*   Plate 105

A large, powerful skink, the Land Mullet is found in the coastal rainforests of southern Queensland and northern New South Wales. It is an extremely shy, swift-moving lizard, making its home in a hollow log or burrow. Like most of the larger species of Australian skinks, the Land Mullet is viviparous, producing about nine live young.

The Land Mullet feeds on insects, snails, mice, and berries. It may reach a length of 75 centimetres and is recognised to be the largest skink in Australia.

Richard's Skink *Egernia richardi*   Plate 106

This large, robust skink is an inhabitant of Arnhem Land, Northern Territory.

It is a shy, diurnal skink, not particularly common in its habitat, and grows to 50 centimetres in length.

Yakka Skink *Egernia rugosa*   Plate 107

An uncommon skink occuring in the dry forests of eastern Queensland, the Yakka Skink lives in small colonies amongst rocky outcrops. It is a robust lizard growing to a maximum length of 45 centimetres.

Little is known of the habits of this secretive skink, but it has been observed feeding upon insects and mice.

Brown Rock Skink *Egernia saxatilis saxatilis*   Plate 108

Although similar in appearance to its close relative the Black Rock Skink (*Egernia saxatilis intermedia*), the Brown Rock Skink may be easily distinguished by its colouration and limited distribution. It is found only in the Warrumbungle Ranges of central New South Wales where it shelters within rock crevices.

This uncommon skink attains a maximum length of 30 centimetres and feeds upon worms and a large variety of insects.

The juveniles of this species measure almost 8 centimetres in length at birth, and are liberally speckled with white on the dorsal surface.

Black Rock Skink *Egernia saxatilis intermedia*   Plate 109

This skink occurs in coastal regions from Victoria to northern New South Wales. It is usually discovered within rock crevices in mountainous country, but it will also shelter beneath loose bark or amongst dead timber.

Although the Black Rock Skink may be regarded as fully grown at a length of 30 centimetres, specimens from the northern part of its distribution often attain a length of 45 centimetres. This robust lizard, which is easily recognisable by its characteristic orange ventral surface, is known to feed upon insects and worms.

Spiny-tailed Skink *Egernia stokesii* Plate 110

A lizard of the central regions of the continent, occurring in all States of the mainland except Victoria, the Spiny-tailed Skink attains a length of 27 centimetres. It is gregarious in habit, living in colonies amongst stony outcrops, but it has also been observed to inhabit hollow trees. The strongly keeled scales and the spiny tail make it difficult to dislodge this lizard from the crevice in which it shelters.

The Spiny-tailed Skink is viviparous, producing about five live young which measure approximately 6 centimetres at birth.

Night Skink *Egernia striata* Plate 111

The strong nocturnal tendencies of this skink are betrayed by its markedly elliptical pupils, a feature most uncommon to skinks. It occurs in the red-sand regions of central-western Australia where it inhabits a burrow in flat country. The burrow usually has a number of exits, which may be covered with a thin crust of sand. This unusual skink grows to approximately 30 centimetres in length.

Tree Skink *Egernia striolata* Plate 112

This secretive lizard occurs west of the Great Dividing Range, from Queensland through New South Wales and Victoria to South Australia. It is usually found in family groups beneath the loose bark of dead trees, but it also inhabits rock crevices. The dead timber in which it shelters offers an abundant supply of insects, which form the basis of its diet.

The Tree Skink is viviparous, normally producing only two or three live young, which measure approximately 6 centimetres at birth. A mature specimen may measure 20 centimetres in length.

White's Skink *Egernia whitii* Plate 113

This active lizard occurs in rocky coastal areas from the border of Queensland and New South Wales to Victoria, Tasmania and South Australia. Its home usually consists of a burrow beneath a large rock, though it may also be found under logs. It is not uncommon to find two or more White's Skinks together in a community burrow.

White's Skink may grow to a length of over 30 centimetres, and its diet consists of insects, worms and berries. It is a viviparous species, producing about four live young.

Banded Skink *Eremiascincus richardsonii* Plate 114

A nocturnal lizard, the Banded Skink occurs throughout the drier areas of mainland Australia, where it shelters in or beneath rotting timber or within a burrow.

It attains a maximum length of 20 centimetres and feeds upon insects, small skinks and geckos, and shows a particular liking for moths. It is exceptionally aggressive in its feeding habits, becoming highly excitable when attracted by the movements of its prey.

Garden Skink *Lampropholis guichenoti* Plate 115

One of the few reptiles that has managed to adapt itself successfully to a suburban existence, the Garden Skink is generally more common in suburban yards and gardens than in its natural state. It is an inhabitant of south-eastern Australia where it shelters on the ground beneath rocks, logs and debris.

Although the Garden Skink lays only two or three eggs, large numbers are often discovered on the one site, this being the result of community egg-laying.

This small lizard attains a maximum length of 10 centimetres, and feeds upon small insects, flies, moths, and worms.

Weasel Skink *Lampropholis mustelina*   Plate 116

The Weasel Skink is most often encountered beneath rotted timber or rocks covering loose soil. It grows to a length of about 12 centimetres and occurs in south-eastern Australia where it is common in some areas. It is occasionally found in suburban yards and gardens, but it is never as prolific in these surroundings as the Garden Skink (*Lampropholis guichenoti*). Small insects and insect larvae form the basis of its diet.

Spotted Skink *Leiolopisma ocellatum*   Plate 117

The Spotted Skink is confined to Tasmania and the Bass Strait islands. It is an inhabitant of rocky areas, sheltering in the crevices afforded by exfoliating rock and basking for long periods at the entrance of its retreat.

An adult Spotted Skink measures approximately 13 centimetres.

Red-throated Skink *Leiolopisma platynotum*   Plate 118

This active skink is often encountered amongst the rocky sandstone ridges of the Sydney area. The brilliant colouring of the throat may vary in intensity with individual specimens, and in some cases is entirely absent. Its diet is restricted to small insects and worms, and it attains a maximum length of about 12 centimetres.

Two-toed Desert Skink *Lerista labialis*   Plate 119

Immediately recognisable as a burrower by its degenerate limbs, the Two-toed Desert Skink inhabits the sandy regions of central Australia. Owing to its subterranean habits it is rarely observed except when uncovered by the moving of a log embedded in the soft red soil. It reaches a maximum length of 10 centimetres and feeds upon minute insects.

Fire-tailed Skink *Morethia taeniopleura* Plate 120

This diminutive, brilliantly coloured skink ranges across most of the northern half of Australia. It is an inhabitant of leaf litter, often in dry rocky areas.

An active, diurnal lizard, the Fire-tailed Skink is fully grown at 8 centimetres.

Three-toed Skink *Saiphos equalis* Plate 121

The Three-toed Skink is a typical burrowing skink, with degenerate limbs and eyes, and a smooth elongated body. It is common on the coast of New South Wales and southern Queensland, where it is usually encountered amongst leaf mould or under rocks or logs covering sandy ground. Once it has been disturbed it is quick to burrow out of sight beneath the loose soil.

A large specimen may measure 15 centimetres. Its diet consists primarily of insect larvae. The breeding habits are interesting in that the female lays up to five eggs containing fully developed young, which subsequently hatch within a few days of being deposited.

Douglas' Skink *Sphenomorphus douglasi* Plate 122

Douglas' Skink is common in the tropical coastal areas of north-western Australia and the Top End of the Northern Territory. It is most active after dark, concealing itself during the day beneath timber covering loose soil. The colouration is variable, the more common phase being sombre brown with darker and lighter markings on the flanks. Douglas' Skink can be considered fully grown at a length of 20 centimetres.

Murray's Skink *Sphenomorphus murrayi* Plate 123

This attractive skink inhabits the coastal rainforests of northern New South Wales and southern Queensland, living beneath logs or rocks embedded in the soft soil. It feeds primarily upon insects, having little difficulty in obtaining a constant supply from among the endless variety inhabiting the rotting vegetation on the forest floor. Murray's Skink is primarily nocturnal, rarely being seen in direct sunlight, and reaches a maximum length of 25 centimetres.

Black-tailed Skink *Sphenomorphus nigricauda*   Plate 124

An inhabitant of the rainforest, the Black-tailed Skink occurs in Cape York Peninsula, north-eastern Queenland, the Torres Strait Islands and New Guinea.

It forages amongst dense leaf litter on the floor of the rainforest, and shelters beneath decomposing timber. It is largely nocturnal, and grows to approximately 15 centimetres in length.

Golden Water Skink *Sphenomorphus quoyii*   Plate 125

A common lizard inhabiting watercourses of eastern and south-eastern Australia, the Golden Water Skink grows to over 30 centimetres in length.

When disturbed while sun-basking by the side of a stream, it will enter the water without hesitation, swimming efficiently to the opposite bank where it usually disappears in a hole or crevice amongst the rocks. In many areas it has adapted itself to a suburban existence, living with apparent contentment in stormwater drains.

This active lizard feeds upon worms, tadpoles, small frogs, and a large variety of insects.

Yellow-bellied Skink *Sphenomorphus tenuis*   Plate 126

A rather uncommon lizard, the Yellow-bellied Skink may be found amongst rocks or beneath loose bark along most of the eastern seaboard of Australia. It often occurs in suburban areas where it conceals itself in the crevices of stone fences. This shy lizard may be observed basking in the sun at the entrance of the crevice, but any disturbance whatsoever will result in its immediate retreat.

The Yellow-bellied Skink attains a maximum length of 20 centimetres and feeds upon small insects.

Gunther's Skink *Tiliqua branchialis* Plate 127

This short-limbed skink grows to a maximum length of 18 centimetres. It is an inhabitant of mostly arid regions throughout Western Australia and South Australia.

Due to the severity of daytime temperature throughout most of its range, Gunther's Skink is largely nocturnal. It shelters by day within porcupine grass or beneath ground debris.

She-oak Skink *Tiliqua casuarinae* Plate 128

The long tail, slender body and degenerate limbs tend to give this lizard a snake-like appearance. Exceptionally aggressive in temperament, it displays marked hostility towards others of its own species. It is an inhabitant of grassy country from the central coast of New South Wales to Victoria and Tasmania.

The She-oak Skink grows to an average maximum length of 30 centimetres though larger specimens are occasionally encountered. The female produces approximately five live young, each of which is a brightly coloured replica of the parent.

Pink-tongued Skink *Tiliqua gerrardii* Plate 129

This strongly clawed skink inhabits coastal rainforests from the Gosford district of New South Wales to Cape York Peninsula, where it shelters beneath the loose bark of trees and in rock crevices. Colouration is highly variable; individual specimens may be strongly banded or lacking in markings at all. It reaches a maximum length of 45 centimetres.

The Pink-tongued Skink is seminocturnal in habit, being particularly active during warm nights. It is selective in its feeding habits, subsisting almost entirely upon a diet of slugs and snails.

The young are born live, a large female producing up to twenty-four. They measure approximately 6 centimetres at birth, and may be strongly banded with pink and black, or plain with a dark band on the head.

Central Blue Tongue *Tiliqua multifasciata*   **Plate 130**

The Central Blue Tongue is somewhat smaller than the Common Blue Tongue (*Tiliqua scincoides scincoides*). It inhabits the arid regions of northern and central Australia and grows to a length of 40 centimetres. It is both diurnal and nocturnal in habit, being active during early morning, late afternoon, and also after sunset.

The Central Blue Tongue is viviparous, producing from two to four live young which measure approximately 10 centimetres at birth.

Blotched Blue Tongue *Tiliqua nigrolutea*   **Plates 131A, 131B**

Perhaps the most brightly coloured of the Blue Tongue lizards, the Blotched Blue Tongue occurs from the Blue Mountains of New South Wales to Victoria, South Australia, the Bass Strait islands and Tasmania. Specimens from the southern areas are smaller and far less brightly coloured than the New South Wales alpine form, which attains a length of 50 centimetres.

This handsome skink feeds upon snails, worms, insects, mice, and native berries. It is viviparous, producing approximately eight live young.

Western Blue Tongue *Tiliqua occipitalis*   **Plate 132**

The Western Blue Tongue is found in dry inland areas of western New South Wales, north-western Victoria, South Australia, and southern Western Australia, where it usually inhabits a rabbit warren. It is feared as being venomous by people in certain areas, where it is often known by the name of "Puff Adder".

It is similar in appearance to the Common Blue Tongue (*Tiliqua scincoides scincoides*), though is easily recognisable, owing to its striking colouration and markings. There is a record of five live young being produced, each of which was strongly banded with yellow and chocolate brown.

The Western Blue Tongue feeds upon insects, snails, and native berries, and grows to a length of 45 centimetres.

Common Blue Tongue *Tiliqua scincoides scincoides*   Plate 133

The Common Blue Tongue occurs throughout eastern Australia, often being encountered in suburban gardens. Contrary to popular belief, it is non-venomous, as are all Australian lizards. At the approach of danger it will invariably choose to retreat, though if cornered it will hiss violently, opening the mouth and protruding the bright-blue tongue in an attempt to frighten its aggressor. It may bite as a last resort, but is capable of inflicting a superficial wound only.

This relatively slow-moving skink reaches a maximum length of 50 centimetres, and its diet consists of snails, insects, mice, and fruit. The Common Blue Tongue is viviparous, producing an average of ten live young, measuring approximately 10 centimetres at birth.

Northern Blue Tongue *Tiliqua scincoides intermedia*   Plate 134

This is the largest of the Blue Tongue lizards, attaining a maximum length of 60 centimetres. It is similar in appearance to the Common Blue Tongue (*Tiliqua scincoides scincoides*), but unlike the former, occurs only in the far north of Western Australia and the Northern Territory.

The Northern Blue Tongue is most active during the early morning and late afternoon, but it may also be found on warm nights. The bright-blue colouring of the tongue, which is regularly protruded by this lizard, has led many to believe that it has venomous qualities. It is in fact non-venomous, and unless provoked is entirely inoffensive.

The Northern Blue Tongue is omnivorous in its feeding habits, devouring insects, worms, mice, and a variety of fruits.

Western Shingleback *Trachydosaurus rugosus rugosus*   Plate 135

The Western Shingleback inhabits the coast and hinterland of Western Australia, excluding the far north. It occurs in a variety of habitats, from arid, sandy plains to wet, coastal heathland.

It is a slow-moving and reasonably inoffensive lizard; however, its powerful jaws are capable of inflicting a painful bite if it is sufficiently provoked. An adult Western Shingleback measures 40 centimetres in length.

Eastern Shingleback *Trachydosaurus rugosus asper*   Plate 136

This well-known lizard is widely distributed in dry inland areas of eastern Australia. The colouration is very variable. In some areas uniform brown is the predominant form, but specimens may be strikingly marked with white or yellow blotches.

The Eastern Shingleback grows to 45 centimetres in length, and feeds largely on ground blossoms and herbage, but it will also devour insects and snails. It is viviparous, usually giving birth to two, rarely one or three, live young, which measure half the length of the adult at birth.

Prickly Forest Skink *Tropidophorus queenslandiae*   Plate 137

This strange, slow-moving skink makes its home beneath damp, rotting logs on the dark floor of the rainforests of far north-eastern Queensland. Little is known of its habits, though it shows obvious discomfort when exposed to direct sunlight.

It reaches a length of 13 centimetres and feeds on worms and soft-bodied insects.

Lizards in Captivity

Collecting

Before any attempt is made to collect lizards, it must be remembered that these reptiles are now protected by law in all States and Territories of Australia. It is therefore necessary to seek the advice of the appropriate wildlife service in the State in which you wish to collect or keep lizards before proceeding. If your search is to be carried out on private property it is obligatory to obtain the permission of the owner before you begin.

For the beginner there are a number of common lizards that will thrive in captivity, making interesting pets, but greater rewards may be won by the more serious enthusiast who is willing to specialise with a particular species or group of lizards with the purpose of observing and recording their habits. There is a great deal to learn about even many common varieties, and the prospect of observing unrecorded data is open to anyone with a little more than the average amount of patience. A keen amateur herpetologist with this purpose can expect more cooperation from the wildlife authority, as well as active advice and encouragement from the staff of the local museum. It is most important to work closely with the museum, for single observations are often meaningless until they have been collected from a variety of sources, and grouped together to be viewed in true perspective. The museum provides an appropriate base for the grouping of this data.

The collecting of lizards can be divided into two main categories, locating the quarry and the actual capture itself. The experienced collector has the advantage of knowing the environmental preferences of the particular lizard he wishes to collect, but unfortunately the beginner is destined to wander through the bush until by chance he is presented with the reptile basking in the sun at his feet.

There are a few species that have managed to survive the spread of civilisation and can be encountered in suburban yards and gardens, but there is a greater possibility of success if you begin your search in the bushland. In the temperate areas lizards can be located by walking slowly and quietly through the bush where they may be found sunning themselves on a rock, log or tree limb, usually within a short distance of their retreat. During winter and on overcast days the most effective method is to turn over rocks, logs, sheets of iron and other ground debris, as well as examining rock crevices and tree hollows with a small torch. All overturned material should be returned to its original position, for the reckless destruction of the habitat will have an adverse effect on the lizard population as well as upon that of any other animals or insects depending on this cover for their livelihood. Some species, notably the geckos, are nocturnal, therefore the only way they will be encountered during daylight hours is by searching beneath cover, in dark rock crevices, or under the loose bark of trees. With the aid of a strong torch it will also be possible to collect geckos after dark during their nocturnal wanderings.

By reading about the particular habits of a lizard that you wish to find you will have a better idea of where to begin the search. Lizards such as the Eastern Water Dragon (*Physignathus lesueurii lesueurii*), are invariably found in close proximity to water, therefore by following the banks of a freshwater creek or river your chances of encountering a Water Dragon will be increased.

In the semidesert and tropical regions lizards are more abundant, but owing to their specialised mode of existence they are usually hard to find. Most species retreat from the heat of the midday sun, and even strictly diurnal forms such as the dragons and monitors are most active during the early morning or late afternoon. The majority of skinks and legless lizards are active during this same period, but will also be found long after nightfall. The turning of rocks and other cover in these areas will generally show negative results, since the majority of species shelter well beneath the ground as a means of insulation from the intense heat of the sun. Owing to the vastness of these particular regions, I have found that the most satisfactory results can be obtained by driving through the area during those hours when the lizards are most active, slowly enough to check the trees, rocks and general area close to the road. After dark many of the nocturnal species will be found by driving in a similar manner on bitumen roads. The road surface retains heat for hours after sundown and many reptiles will be attracted to it for this reason.

In the dry areas where porcupine grass is prolific, large clumps often provide the home for a variety of animals and insects, including lizards, most of which are rarely encountered outside this particular environment. Another favoured haunt of the desert reptiles is within large termite mounds, which are very abundant in many areas. By dismantling one you will find that the maze of tunnels and caverns of the interior often provides a home for a variety of lizards, notably geckos, but also skinks such as the Depressed Spiny Skink (*Egernia depressa*).

Most lizards in the desert areas choose to live beneath the soft red soil. A thorough search in a suitable area will reveal the entrances to numerous small burrows in and around the stunted vegetation, but unfortunately the majority will be empty. It is generally possible to determine whether or not a specific burrow is currently in use by the presence of fresh tracks and a well-worn entrance lacking spider-web or debris. The soft nature of the soil allows for excavation with little difficulty, but where possible it should be done by hand, since a shovel may damage the lizard inside. Some of these burrowing lizards have become highly adapted to this particular environment, their burrows often being extensive, with a number of rear entrances. These entrances are frequently hidden from view amongst vegetation, or they may be covered by a thin crust of sand, enabling the inhabitant to escape unnoticed while the digging is in process.

The hollows, crevices and loose bark of trees provide the shelter necessary for a number of arboreal lizards. In the north of Australia the Spotted Tree Monitor (*Varanus timorensis similis*) may often be observed on the trunk or low branches of a tree, where it waits for a suitable insect or small lizard to wander within range. When approached it will generally ascend the tree and disappear into a hollow section. A smaller monitor, Gillen's Pigmy Monitor (*Varanus gilleni*) of central Australia, can be found by removing the loose bark of dead mulga trees. Within its territory a lizard will have an accurate knowledge of the various means of retreat available and will instinctively make for the safety of one of these when alarmed. Although a few varieties are sufficiently slow-moving to give the collector little difficulty, the majority can move very quickly over a short distance, and they are usually found close to their particular burrow, rock crevice or tree, depending on the species concerned. If the lizard reaches its destination the protection afforded will often be sufficient to make capture a difficult if not possible task.

There is a range of equipment used by experienced collectors in the capture of lizards that would otherwise prove to be very difficult; each item has its own particular application.

Noosing Pole

The noosing pole is a length of strong, light material such as bamboo, aluminium or fibreglass, with a slip noose attached securely to the end. It can be effectively employed in capturing the swifter-moving dragons and monitors, which will generally take flight before you can get close enough to catch them by other means. The opened noose is simply slipped over the head of the lizard, which in most cases will show no concern during this operation, and is then tightened by a slight pull on the pole. As long as the tension is retained and the cord is strong enough, the lizard will not free itself once the noose has tightened. As a long pole will prove cumbersome while travelling through the bush, it is advantageous for it to be made up of attachable sections that can be quickly assembled and dismantled like those of an ordinary fishing rod. On the tip of the pole there should be two nooses of different strengths affixed, so that you will be ready for a lizard of any size that may cross your path. The lighter noose should be of a strong, thin twine, and the other of a heavy-gauge fishing line. Either one can be held back when not in use by adhesive tape.

Prodding Wires

Two lengths of a strong but pliable wire can be very helpful in coaxing a lizard from the shelter of a rock crevice or tree hollow. By prodding the sensitive areas behind the limbs, it is sometimes possible to dislodge the lizard from the inaccessible reaches of the crevice and bring it out into the open. Care must be taken during this operation not to harm the lizard. Occasionally a lizard will resist the most determined efforts, and in this case it should be allowed to retain its freedom.

Crowbar

With the aid of a small crowbar it is possible to lift a large rock that may be too heavy to raise by hand. After lifting it a few inches with the bar, a small rock can be inserted to hold the position, which will enable the collector to see underneath. Following this the small piece should be removed, and the rock returned to its original position. Many varieties of lizard favour this particular habitat, therefore damage to the rock under which they shelter should be avoided at all times.

Bow Saw

Without this particular piece of equipment the capture of the majority of tree monitors would prove to be very difficult. The hollow section of the tree where the lizard seeks shelter when alarmed can easily be removed with the aid of this saw, and this section can be subsequently sawn into smaller pieces to enable the lizard to be extracted. It is light, and can be operated with little difficulty in the treetops.

Torch

A strong torch with a wide, even beam is necessary when attempting to collect after nightfall. All geckos and many varieties of skinks and legless lizards are nocturnal, and in certain areas a search after dark will show better results than during the daylight hours. A number of diurnal lizards may also be found in the open on a warm night, a notable example being Merten's Water Monitor (*Varanus mertensi*), which can be collected after dark by torchlight while it sleeps on a branch overhanging the water. A small penlight torch is invaluable during daylight collecting for searching the dark recesses of a rock crevice or hollow log.

Bags and Boxes

The safest and most effective way of transporting the lizard after capture is in a collecting bag specially designed for this purpose. The bags can be made in a variety of sizes to suit particular lizards, but should always adhere to the same basic proportions, that is, an approximate depth to width ratio of two to one. Because of its strength and relatively low cost, unbleached calico is perhaps the most suitable material to use. All seams should be double sewn, since the lizard will take advantage of any weak spot in its efforts to escape. Two strips of tape can be affixed at the top of the bag, so that the opening can be tied securely after the lizard has been placed inside. For the larger, strongly clawed species a bag made of light canvas should be used in preference to a hessian sack, which may cause injury to the lizard inside. The nature of the material will allow sufficient ventilation within the bag and the lizard will remain in perfect health in this manner for as long as two or three days, provided the temperature is kept at a satisfactory level. It is possible to confine more than one lizard in a bag, but overcrowding should be avoided.

If the collecting trip extends to a week or more, and particularly if the lizards are to be kept in a car for this period, far greater efforts are necessary to ensure their safe transportation. In the case of small delicate lizards, particularly geckos, which cannot be confined in a bag for this length of time, a small ventilated box with a quantity of leaf mould or loose earth inside is necessary. A few drops of water can be added occasionally to prevent dehydration. The lizards in the bags should be housed in a larger box to keep them separated from the mountains of equipment which will have to be carried in the vehicle. This box should again be well ventilated, and with the aid of shelving inside, the piling of bags on top of each other can be avoided. It is important that the box be sheltered from the sun and also that it does not come into contact with any section of the vehicle heated by the exhaust system. Each day the reptiles should be removed from their bags and given the opportunity to drink. The temperature inside the car will rise rapidly when it is stopped in the sun, therefore unless shade is available it is inadvisable to stop for longer than a few moments.

Records

Keeping a written record of each specimen collected is of fundamental importance. Such details as date, species, time of day, location of capture, immediate habitat, temperature, dimensions, and sex (where definable), can be used as a basis for your capture records, which can be followed by notes on your observations of the specimen while in captivity, such as rate of growth, quantity of food taken, and frequency of skin-shedding.

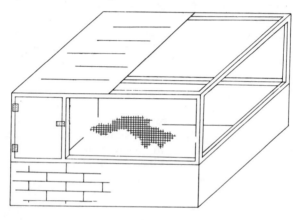

Outside Enclosure

Housing

If the lizards you have chosen to keep have been collected in your own general area, then your task will be a relatively easy one, since you will not need to create an artificial environment. These local lizards can be kept in an outside enclosure where they will be subject to the same climatic conditions as in the wild state.

The size of the enclosure is not unduly important, but should be relative to the number of lizards you intend to keep, and the interior should be designed to duplicate, as far as possible, the environmental preferences of the lizards concerned. If you are keeping Eastern Water Dragons, for example, a large pond will be required within the enclosure for these lizards to remain in a contented state.

In constructing the enclosure a number of important standards must be adhered to.

1. It must be soundly built and escape proof.

2. Wire netting should not be extended to the ground level, since this will encourage the lizard to try continually to escape, and as a result, it will injure itself.

3. The wall of the enclosure should continue at least 45 centimetres below ground level to prevent the lizards from burrowing out.

4. The position of the enclosure should be such that the lizards will receive a liberal amount of sunshine during the course of the day.

5. One section of the enclosure must be sheltered from the wet weather, so that at least one quarter of the ground area remains perfectly dry at all times. By building up the level in this area and providing shelter, you will be assuring the lizards of a dry retreat during wet weather.

If you desire to keep tropical varieties, or lizards from the desert regions, then unless you live in these areas the lizards must be kept indoors and provided with artificial heat and lighting. A very successful indoor reptile enclosure, or vivarium as it is called, can be had by utilising an aquarium equipped with a ventilated cover. A glass-fronted case constructed of wood or aluminium will also prove satisfactory, and may be built to the exact size and requirements you wish.

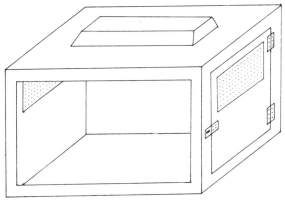

Simple Vivarium

The temperature that a particular lizard will find acceptable is variable and may have to be determined on a trial-and-error basis: however, most species from the warmer regions will thrive when provided with an even temperature between 24°C and 29°C. The heat as well as light can be supplied by an ordinary light bulb, but a bulb designed primarily for heating rather than lighting will prove more satisfactory for this purpose, since it will generate more heat for the same amount of wattage. Bulbs of different wattage can be tested, using a maximum-minimum thermometer, until you are able to determine the correct one needed to bring your particular vivarium to the required temperature, or you may regulate the temperature with a thermostat.

For the nocturnal varieties it is possible to simulate night and day by using a white and a blue bulb. The lizards will remain concealed during the day while the white light is in use, venturing forth at night under the blue light, which will enable you to feed and observe them under natural conditions.

In designing the interior of the vivarium, regardless of what varieties you intend to house, it will be necessary to provide a place where they can conceal themselves from view. Most lizards are shy and retiring by nature, and unless some form of shelter is available they will never settle down in captivity. With the aid of natural materials and plants it will be possible to decorate the inside of the vivarium so that it will be an attraction in any room, as well as meeting the requirements of the lizards kept within it. A desert setting can be arranged by using red sand, a sun-bleached log, bare rock and small desert plants or grass, which can in fact be growing from a small pot concealed beneath the sand. A miniature rainforest can be set up with the aid of moss-covered rocks and logs and an array of suitable plants. The plants and moss will need to be watered regularly, but it must be remembered that the shelter you have provided, perhaps in the form of a hollow log, should always be kept dry. For lizards that shelter amongst rock crevices, an environment can be reproduced in miniature by using small flat stones, which can be built up round the walls of the vivarium and fixed into place with cement. To retain a natural effect the cement can be tinted to match the colour of the rock in use.

Fortunately few Australian lizards require a semiaquatic vivarium; this is the one most likely to cause problems. Basically the semiaquatic vivarium is an aquarium half-filled with water and provided with up to fifty per cent land space.

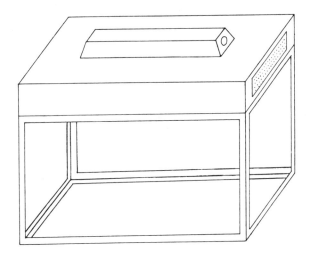

Aquarium-Vivarium

The major problem to overcome is that of keeping the water clean. If you have one or two small lizards only, in a large aquarium, a strong aquarium filter will do this job quite adequately, but with a larger lizard the daily fouling of the water will generally be too great for a filter to cope with; so unless you are willing to change the water each day you should think carefully before you choose a semiaquatic lizard to keep. The most appropriate land surface would be a single rock of a suitable size, which would present the least difficulty in cleaning the aquarium. A number of logs may be fixed into position to overhang the water, one of which can be hollow, therefore providing the necessary shelter for the inhabitants. The appearance can be further enhanced with the addition of plants both in and out of the water. In addition to a light bulb, a thermostatically controlled aquarium heater will generally be necessary in order to keep the water temperature at a constant level.

Food and Feeding

In order to maintain your lizards in a healthy state, they must be supplied with an adequate amount of nourishing food. Most are very selective in their feeding habits, and unless their dietary requirements are met they will not survive in captivity. Whenever possible natural food should be given; however, some lizards will readily accept substitute food and will in fact thrive on many of the items we include in our own diet.

All Australian lizards are primarily carnivorous, feeding upon almost any live food they can overpower. Rats and mice are a popular addition to the diet of most larger lizards, and are readily available from most pet centres. A more satisfactory and less expensive alternative is to maintain your own breeding colony, which will provide a constant supply in a full range of size from newborn to adult. When given an adequate amount of space, food and water, both rats and mice will multiply at a surprising rate, but care must be taken not to overtax their breeding capacity by feeding off more than the colony is able to produce. Large monitors will readily accept birds. These can be supplied in the form of "day-old chicks", which are available at reasonable rates as "seconds" from the hatcheries. Surplus amounts of rats, mice, or birds can be stored frozen in a refrigerator, to be thawed out and fed as required. Some lizards, however, are unwilling to feed unless stimulated by the movement of their prey, and therefore will not accept food in this form. Frogs, snails, worms, and insects can generally be collected in large amounts in the field or garden during the greater part of the year, but during the winter they will become increasingly difficult to procure. Certain insects can be bred in captivity for the purpose of supplying a constant source of insect food throughout the year. The most popular of these is perhaps the larva of a small black beetle, commonly known as the mealworm. The colony can be started with a hundred or so mealworms housed in a well-ventilated container with a quantity of oatmeal or bran, interspersed with a few layers of hessian or similar material. Before long the worms will turn into pupae, and from these will emerge the black beetles, which will deposit their eggs and die shortly afterwards. A lettuce leaf or a few thin slices of potato

Lizard	Natural Food	Substitute Food
Large Monitors	rats, mice, birds	raw meat, liver, fish, eggs
Small Monitors	mice, frogs, insects, small lizards, worms	raw meat, liver, fish, eggs
Large Skinks	snails, mice, worms, insects, dandelion blossoms	raw meat, liver, fish, eggs, milk, banana, lettuce, pear, tomato, apple, etc.
Small Skinks	insects, worms, mealworms	raw meat, liver, fish, eggs, milk, banana, lettuce, pear, tomato, apple, etc.
Geckos	insects, worms, mealworms	Some geckos will eat a small quantity of honey, jam, or soft fruit.
Large Dragons	mice, insects, worms, small lizards, dandelion blossoms	Few dragons will accept substitute food, but the Eastern Water Dragon will usually eat raw meat or fruit.
Small Dragons	insects, worms, mealworms	Nil
Legless Lizards	insects, mealworms, small lizards	soft fruit, eggs

can be dampened and placed beneath each layer of hessian to supply moisture for the growing worms. When these have been eaten or have dried up, fresh ones must be added, but do not remove any of the dried slices as they may contain eggs. Mealworms are not seasonal breeders; they will multiply continuously throughout the year under ideal conditions. To safeguard against severely depleting the population of the colony it is advisable to have a number of separate colonies in operation simultaneously, each to be used in turn on a rotating basis.

The chart on p. 63 will outline the type of food that each group of lizards will be most likely to accept. "Insects" can be taken to include not only grasshoppers, crickets, beetles, cockroaches, moths, flies, cicadas and other insects, but also spiders and centipedes.

There are no strict rules determining the frequency of feeding or the quantity of food to be given; the feeding schedule can be relatively flexible. It will usually be sufficient to feed large lizards twice a week, but smaller lizards will require more regular attention. Use your own judgement when feeding each particular lizard; do not allow any loss of condition, for this is often irreversible. It is equally dangerous to overfeed, but this can be difficult to prevent when a number of lizards are housed together, for at least one member will always be bolder than its companions. Occasionally a lizard will be unwilling to lead a captive existence and will resist the most determined efforts to induce it to feed. In this case it should be released in its natural environment to avoid a slow death by starvation.

Fresh water should be available in the lizard enclosure or vivarium at all times. A heavy, shallow bowl is best, as it is less likely to be upset by the inhabitants.

Maintaining Health

If the suggestions in the "housing" and "feeding" sections of this chapter are followed closely, the good health of the lizard will usually follow as a matter of course. Most common ailments can be traced to vitamin deficiency due to an insufficient or unsatisfactory food supply, inadequate heating, excessive dampness or crowded and dirty conditions. Cleanliness within the vivarium should be maintained at all times. Uneaten food or faeces must be removed and any spilled water mopped up without delay. In addition, the vivarium should be cleaned and disinfected throughout on a regular basis. The inhabitants can be removed and held in collecting bags while this operation is in process.

Respiratory infections will generally afflict lizards that are subjected to cold or damp conditions. The most apparent symptoms are difficulty in breathing and a discharge of mucus from the nose and mouth. If caught in the early stages this ailment can generally be cured by increasing the temperature, and by treatment with one of the sulpha drugs, which your chemist will usually supply once their purpose has been explained. Dosage will depend upon size, varying from a quarter of a tablet a day for small lizards to a full tablet for very large specimens. Administration of the tablet will often prove difficult, but by persevering it can be introduced to the side of the mouth and pushed to the back of the throat with a smooth object, such as a plastic spoon, which will be least likely to damage the mouth.

The causes of the mouth infection commonly encountered in captive reptiles are not fully understood; however, it is probable that it begins with a slight injury or abrasion within the mouth. Affected areas of the mouth will be identifiable by a thick yellow scum, which may spread rapidly to the throat and cause the death of the specimen if left unchecked. Treatment can be effected by physically removing as much of the scum as possible and applying a solution of one part Listerine and two parts water to the interior of the mouth twice daily. If this treatment fails to bring a response, an antibiotic powder such as Neosporin can be applied to the affected areas as an alternative method.

Skin infections are almost invariably due to damp conditions within the enclosure; it is therefore necessary to isolate an affected lizard in dry quarantine quarters as a prelude to treatment. The dead scales and infection are easily removed with the aid of tweezers, and if this is followed with daily treatment of Neosporin antibiotic powder or cream, positive results will generally be attained. Skin problems may also arise as a result of the inability of a lizard to shed sections of its skin, caused by the natural oil beneath the skin drying up. No attempt should be made to remove the skin while it is still firmly affixed to the body, since this may have serious consequences. After soaking the specimen in a bath of tepid water for a few hours the skin will usually come away with little effort.

Worms or other similar internal parasites are present to some degree in most lizards. In its natural environment, and in peak condition, a lizard is able to carry these parasites with no apparent complications, but with the shock of captivity and confinement, and the resultant slight loss of condition and stamina, these parasites will occasionally multiply swiftly, causing a rapid loss of condition and death within a very short time. There is very little that can be done in the form of treatment; it is more important to ensure that your lizards are in a healthy state, and that any new arrivals are subjected to a minimum of interference and handling.

Mites are introduced to a collection on a new arrival, usually from another collector, therefore each new acquisition should be checked carefully or quarantined before coming into contact with the rest of your collection. Having been introduced they will multiply rapidly within the confined space of a vivarium and pose a serious threat to the health of the inhabitants. Raised scales are ominous signs of the presence of mites; examination with a magnifying glass will often show them hiding beneath. On a heavily infested specimen the mite droppings will be visible as tiny white specks on the scales. Mites can be effectively eradicated by thoroughly spraying the specimen, the vivarium and its contents with a solution of Neguvon powder and water, approximately one teaspoon of Neguvon to 2½ cups of water. As an added precaution the spraying should be repeated after a lapse of a few days. An equally effective measure is the use of a Shelltox pest-strip, which is simply hung in the vivarium, out of reach of the inhabitants, for a period of a few days.

Ticks will occasionally be present on recently captured lizards. A drop of methylated spirits will loosen their hold, after which they can be removed with tweezers.

Breeding

When a lizard produces eggs or young in captivity it is generally the result of a mating in the wild state, for lizards will rarely mate and subsequently produce young successfully in captivity. This is not to suggest that it is impossible, but it is necessary for the lizards to be entirely content with their surroundings for any chance of success.

A lizard in a gravid state must be removed from the enclosure and isolated, for soon after the young are born or eggs produced they may be eaten or damaged by larger lizards in the enclosure. In addition, the young or eggs should be separated from the mother with the least possible delay, for she may also constitute a danger. Juvenile lizards are entirely self-reliant at birth; the mother has no postnatal maternal instincts.

Most lizards lay eggs, and their successful incubation is not a task to be taken lightly. They should be collected immediately after they have been laid and buried in loose sandy soil in a ventilated plastic container. The surface of the soil should be covered with a piece of towelling, which must be kept in a slightly moist condition. This can usually be accomplished with just a few drops of water a day. The eggs can be examined each week and any that have shrivelled or gone mouldy removed. The position of the healthy eggs must not be altered, since this can affect the developing embryo inside. A fairly even temperature of approximately 27°C will ensure the maximum possibility of successful hatching. Particular attention must be paid to the diet of newborn lizards, for it is this period of rapid growth that is the most important stage of their development.

Photographing Lizards

Although lizards present a somewhat more difficult subject to the wildlife photographer than do most other Australian fauna, anyone willing to devote the necessary amount of time and effort to this particular field will find both his subjects and the photographic results attained to be infinitely rewarding. The number of varieties available is virtually inexhaustible, and the diversity of colour, size and form amongst the Australian lizards will provide the keen photographer with a more than interesting subject.

The most important factor in photographing reptiles is to overcome the inherent fear that unfortunately affects the majority of people. I have perhaps been working at an advantage in this regard, since I had been collecting and studying reptiles in an amateur capacity for almost ten years before I began to record my specimens on film. However suitable a stroll through the bush with your camera and 400-millimetre lens may have been in your approach to standard wildlife photography, I am afraid that this attitude will be ineffective if your subject is to be lizards. Each lizard photographed in this book has first been captured, and with few exceptions a lens of standard focal length has been used. General opinion would have it that reptiles are best photographed with a suitable barrier between photographer and subject, whether it be distance or a concrete wall, and that the equipment required is a range of lenses with a focal length of 200 millimetres upwards. I have found it necessary, however, to be close to the subject at all times, which enables me to manoeuvre, or attempt to manoeuvre, the lizard into the correct position in relation to the background and the light source, hence the reason for a standard focal length lens (50-55 millimetres).

Equipment

Camera

The most important piece of equipment necessary is a single-lens reflex camera capable of accepting interchangeable lenses. For ease of handing I recommend the 35-millimetre format. My opinion is that any of the 35-millimetre SLR cameras on the market today are adequate, but I regard those with a bayonet-mount lens-fitting system as having a distinct advantage over the screw-in type. The speed of lens interchanging is more than halved by the bayonet mount and the lens tends to fit the camera body more securely. As expense is usually an accurate guide to quality, I should advise a beginner to select the most expensive camera that he or she can afford, but, even more important, to try the camera and be certain that it "fits" in the hand and that the controls can be operated with minimum effort. As the majority of your subjects will require you to go further than the minimum focusing distance on your camera, the next step is to acquire a provision for close-up photography. I use an auto macro lens as standard equipment, which enables me to photograph subjects in a continuous range from life size to infinity at the touch of the focusing ring. This is by far the most satisfactory method, but unfortunately a good lens of this type is expensive. The other method is extension rings, a set of which are relatively inexpensive, and when placed between the camera and the lens reduce the minimum focusing distance by a varying degree in relation to the size of the ring used. The disadvantages of extension rings are unfortunately very apparent to anyone who has been forced to use them extensively. While you are juggling with the rings to compose the picture accurately, and calculating the exposure allowance made necessary by the loss of light entering the camera when this method is used, the subject can very often be making its escape or dozing in the sun with its eyes closed. I do not recommend the employment of a teleconverter or a set of auxiliary close-up lenses, since the result is quite often not of the required standard. It is of some advantage to include in your equipment a lens of approximately 100 millimetres, which may be used occasionally when a lizard objects to the camera at close quarters. I do not use a tripod; I find them far too restrictive in this particular field of photography.

Film

Black-and-white or colour-negative film will not in my opinion reproduce the subject to the full advantage, and for this reason I advise the use of colour-positive (colour-slide) film. As many of your photographs will be close-ups, a film with a higher ASA rating will be more practical, to enable you to gain maximum depth of field by using a smaller aperture setting. I am satisfied with the results I achieve using Ektachrome 100, but this is more or less a case of personal taste and I should think that most other films would prove satisfactory.

Light Source

There are only two suitable methods of illumination, direct sunlight or electronic flash. A flash unit is invaluable when photographing many of the nocturnal varieties which are incapable of remaining motionless in direct sunlight for any length of time. For photographing in sunlight using Ektachrome 100, the required exposure will be f11 at 125th of a second or f8 at 250, depending on the stability of the hand. If the available light is insufficient to gain a reading of at least f8 at 125th, then the resultant loss of depth of field will necessitate the use of electronic flash as the alternative. Don't be afraid to use film; I usually find it necessary to take a minimum of ten shots of a lizard to gain a single photograph of the required standard. Vary the aperture settings within a stop either side of the suggested reading while shooting — this is especially important when using flash — and also alter your shooting angle slightly with each shot, for you can never be certain of the success of a photograph until the film has been returned from processing.

As most of your work will be at close quarters to the subject one of the smaller flash units will be most suitable and also less expensive. Owing to the fact that most of my photographs are taken in the field, and that a field trip may extend over a number of weeks, I have found it necessary to select a flash unit powered by removable penlight batteries rather than one with a plug-in rechargeable cell. The disadvantage of the removable battery type is in the rather lengthy recycling period. A flash mounted on the normal accessory shoe on the camera body is entirely unsatisfactory for close-up work, and the various flash brackets generally available are of little more use. My flash bracket is a twin, capable of holding a flash unit on either side of the camera; this is very useful in softening the harsh shadows which are often the result of using a single flash. An important fact to remember when using twin flash is to position one flash unit so that it is farther from the subject than the other; the closer flash serves to illuminate the subject and the farther one will lighten the shadow areas. If both flash units are positioned at an equal distance from the subject, an unnatural double shadow effect may be the result. My flash bracket was manufactured to my own specifications from 25 mm × 6 mm aluminium strip. It is light and easily dismantled and has proved very satisfactory for its purpose

Composing the Picture

The framing of the subject through the viewfinder is the decisive factor between a photograph and a good photograph. Always remember to position the subject amid natural surroundings, minus footprints, bottle-tops and other distractions, but be sure that the background does not distract attention from the actual subject itself. Background materials can be kept at home and used when it is impractical to photograph in the field. I always have a supply of red sand, as well as leaves and native grasses, logs, bark and rock of different kinds on hand for use whenever necessary. When positioning the lizard in your frame fill the frame with the subject; but exerting a degree of patience it is generally possible to manipulate the head, limbs and tail into the exact position you require. Always focus on the eye, and be certain that it is well illuminated. When photographing in sunlight, position the lizard in relation to the sun so that the entire body is illuminated and free from distracting shadows.

The most rewarding aspect of lizard photography, but also the most difficult, is attempting to record on film the specimen while in the process of a natural act, such as feeding, mating, depositing eggs, or shedding skin. As I have mentioned earlier in this chapter, it is next to impossible to photograph lizards satisfactorily in the wild state, but it would be even more difficult to persuade the subject to perform on being removed from its retreat and placed before the camera. The solution is to house the specimen in a vivarium designed for the express purpose of photographing the lizard inside with minimum difficulty. The interior of the photographic vivarium should be decorated to duplicate the occupant's natural environment as far as possible, both for the sake of the lizard, which will settle down more readily, and for the effect of authenticity that it will lend the finished photograph. The rear and side walls should be disguised in such a way that, regardless of what position the subject takes up within the vivarium, the background will appear to be natural. The greatest problem to overcome is that of reflection and distortion, which is often created by the glass between the subject and the camera. By following the rules listed below, however, it will become a simple process.

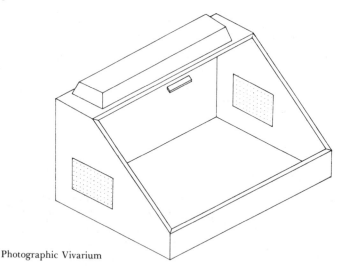

Photographic Vivarium

1. As far as possible hold the camera at an angle of approximately ninety degrees to the plane of the glass front.

2. Dim the room light so that the illumination inside the vivarium is stonger than that outside.

3. Direct the flash unit or units at approximately forty-five degrees to the plane of the glass front. If the vivarium occupies a permanent position in the room, it will be advantageous to have a permanent position for the flash unit, which can be ascertained on a trial-and-error basis, so that you can be assured of a correct exposure and concentrate on composing the picture.

4. Position the flash heads outside the area directly opposite the area that will fall within the frame.

With all the equipment in place, you may sit back comfortably and wait for the lizard to settle into its natural routine.

While photographing, especially in the field, it is a good idea to enlist the help of a friend in dissuading the subject from making an escape, for the majority of our lizards are capable of a determined burst of speed when necessary, and it is very disconcerting to find, on looking through the viewfinder after the necessary adjustments have been made to the camera, that the object of all the effort has departed!

1. Clawless Gecko *Crenadactylus ocellatus* (Halls Creek, WA)
2. Banded Gecko *Cyrtodactylus louisiadensis* (Cooktown, Qld)

3

4A

3. Byrne's Gecko *Diplodactylus byrnei* (Bedourie, Qld)
4A. Spiny-tailed Gecko *Diplodactylus ciliaris* (Mataranka, NT)

4B

5

4B. Spiny-tailed Gecko *Diplodactylus ciliaris* (Port Hedland, WA)
5. Fat-tailed Gecko *Diplodactylus conspicillatus* (Charters Towers, Qld)

6

7

6. Jewelled Gecko *Diplodactylus elderi* (Renmark, SA)
7. Steindachner's Gecko *Diplodactylus steindachneri* (Wilcannia, NSW)

8. Crowned Gecko *Diplodactylus stenodactylus* (Wyndham, WA)
9. White-striped Gecko *Diplodactylus taeniatus* (Port Hedland, WA)

10. Golden-tailed Gecko *Diplodactylus taenicauda* (south-eastern Qld)
11. Tesselated Gecko *Diplodactylus tesselatus* (Walgett, NSW)

12

13

12. Stone Gecko *Diplodactylus vittatus* (Sydney, NSW)
13. Soft-spined Gecko *Diplodactylus williamsi* (Goondiwindi, Qld)

14. House Gecko *Gehyra australis* (Darwin, NT)
15. Pilbara Spotted Dtella *Gehyra fenestra* (Port Hedland, WA)

16. Arnhem Land Spotted Dtella *Gehyra pamela* (Kakadu National Park, NT)
17. Dtella *Gehyra variegata* (Wilcannia, NSW)

18. Asian House Gecko *Hemidactylus frenatus* (Darwin, NT)
19. Prickly Gecko *Heteronotia binoei* (Wilcannia, NSW)

20

21

20. Desert Cave Gecko *Heteronotia spelea* (Northern Territory)
21. Beaded Gecko *Lucasium damaeum* (Wilcannia, NSW)

22. Spiny Knob-tailed Gecko *Nephrurus asper* (Alice Springs, NT)
23. Central Knob-tailed Gecko *Nephrurus levis levis* (Wilcannia, NSW)

24

25

24. Pilbara Knob-tailed Gecko *Nephrurus levis pilbarensis* (Port Hedland, WA)
25. Southern Knob-tailed Gecko *Nephrurus stellatus* (Eyre Peninsula, SA)

26. Castelnaui's Gecko *Oedura castelnaui* (Charters Towers, Qld)
27. Cogger's Velvet Gecko *Oedura coggeri* (Mount Garnet, Qld)

28

29

8. Jewelled Velvet Gecko *Oedura gemmata* (Christmas Creek, NT)
9. Lesueur's Gecko *Oedura lesueurii* (Sydney, NSW)

30. Velvet Gecko *Oedura marmorata* (Katherine, NT)
31. Blotched Gecko *Oedura monilis* (Warrumbungle Ranges, NSW)

32

33

32. Zig-zag Gecko *Oedura rhombifer* (Darwin, NT)
33. Robust Gecko *Oedura robusta* (Warrumbungle Ranges, NSW)

34. Tryon's Gecko *Oedura tryoni* (Moonbi, NSW)
35. Marbled Gecko *Phyllodactylus marmoratus* (Renmark, SA)

36. Leaf-tailed Gecko *Phyllurus cornutus* (Coffs Harbour, NSW)
37. Broad-tailed Rock Gecko *Phyllurus platurus* (Sydney, NSW)

38

39

38. Giant Cave Gecko *Pseudothecadactylus lindneri* (Kakadu National Park, NT)
39. Beaked Gecko *Rhynchoedura ornata* (Wilcannia, NSW)

40. Thick-tailed Gecko *Underwoodisaurus milii* (Wilcannia, NSW)
41. *Delma inornata* (Warren, NSW)

42. Sharp-snouted Legless Lizard *Delma nasuta* (Halls Creek, WA)
43. *Delma tincta* (Darwin, NT)

44A

44B

44A. Burton's Legless Lizard *Lialis burtonis* (Port Hedland, WA)
44B. Burton's Legless Lizard *Lialis burtonis* (Darwin, NT)

45

46

45. Common Scaly Foot *Pygopus lepidopodus* (Sydney, NSW)
46. Black-headed Scaly Foot *Pygopus nigriceps* (Port Hedland, WA)

47

47. Mountain Dragon *Amphibolurus* *diemensis* (Waterfall, NSW)

48

48. Jacky Lizard *Amphibolurus muricatus* (Sydney, NSW)

49. Nobbi *Amphibolurus nobbi* (Ravenshoe, Qld)
50. Chameleon Dragon *Chelosania brunnea* (Jim Jim, NT)

51

51. Frilled Lizard *Chlamydosaurus kingii* (Darwin, NT)

52. Ring-tailed Dragon *Ctenophorus caudicinctus* (Roebourne, WA)
53. Tawny Dragon *Ctenophorus decresii* (SA)

54

55

54. Peninsula Dragon *Ctenophorus fionni* (Eyre Peninsula, SA)
55. Netted Dragon *Ctenophorus nuchalis* (Alice Springs, NT)

56

57

56. Ornate Dragon *Ctenophorus ornatus* (Canning Dam, WA)
57. Painted Dragon *Ctenophorus pictus* (Wilcannia, NSW)

58. Boyd's Forest Dragon *Gonocephalus boydii* (Atherton, Qld)
59. Rainforest Dragon *Gonocephalus spinipes* (Coffs Harbour, NSW)

60. Gilbert's Dragon *Lophognathus gilberti* (Mount Isa, Qld)
61. Long-nosed Water Dragon *Lophognathus longirostris* (Port Hedland, WA)

62

62. Northern Water Dragon *Lophognathus temporalis* (Darwin, NT)

63

64

53. Thorny Devil *Moloch horridus* (Alice Springs, NT)
54. Eastern Water Dragon *Physignathus lesueurii lesueurii* (Ourimbah, NSW)

65

66

65. Gippsland Water Dragon *Physignathus lesueurii howittii* (Nowra, NSW)
66. Western Bearded Dragon *Pogona minima* (Perth, WA)

67

67. Inland Bearded Dragon *Pogona vitticeps* (Wilcannia, NSW)

68

68. Earless Dragon *Tympanocryptis cephalus* (central Australia)

69A

69B

69A. Spiny-tailed Monitor *Varanus acanthurus* (Katherine, NT)
69B. Spiny-tailed Monitor *Varanus acanthurus* (Kakadu National Park, NT)

70. Short-tailed Monitor *Varanus brevicauda* (Roebourne, WA)
71. Stripe-tailed Monitor *Varanus caudolineatus* (Mount Magnet, WA)

72

73

72. Desert Pygmy Monitor *Varanus eremius* (Barkly Tableland, NT)

73. Perenty *Varanus giganteus* (Alice Springs, NT)

74. Gillen's Pigmy Monitor *Varanus gilleni* (Alice Springs, NT)
75. Glauert's Monitor *Varanus glauerti* (Kununurra, WA)

76

77

76. Black-palmed Rock Monitor *Varanus glebopalma* (Graveside Gorge, Kakadu National Park, NT)

77. Gould's Monitor *Varanus gouldii gouldii* (Wilcannia, NSW)

78. Central Sand Monitor *Varanus gouldii flavirufus* (Tennant Creek, NT)
79. Mangrove Monitor *Varanus indicus* (Cape York Peninsula, Qld)

80

81

80. King's Monitor *Varanus kingorum* (Kununurra, WA)
81. Merten's Water Monitor *Varanus mertensi* (Darwin, NT)

82. Mitchell's Water Monitor *Varanus mitchelli* (Katherine River, NT)
83. *Varanus panoptes* (Kimberley Ranges, WA)

84

85

84. Green Tree Monitor *Varanus prasinus* (Port Moresby, PNG)
85. Ridge-tailed Monitor *Varanus primordius* (Pine Creek, NT)

86. Rusty Monitor *Varanus semiremex* (Rockhampton, Qld)

87A

87B

87A. Spencer's Monitor *Varanus spenceri* (Camooweal, Qld)
87B. Spencer's Monitor *Varanus spenceri* (Juvenile)

88. Storr's Monitor *Varanus storri* (Charters Towers, Qld)
89. Spotted Tree Monitor *Varanus timorensis similis* (Hughenden, Qld)

90. Black-headed Monitor *Varanus tristis tristis* (Tennant Creek, NT)
91. Freckled Monitor *Varanus tristis orientalis* (Moline Rock Hole, NT)

92A. Lace Monitor *Varanus varius* (Ivanhoe, NSW)
92B. Lace Monitor *Varanus varius* (Ivanhoe, NSW)

93

94

93. Jewelled Four-fingered Skink *Carlia jarnoldae* (Mount Garnet, Qld)
94. Legless Skink *Coeranoscincus frontalis* (Atherton, Qld)

95

96

95. Fence Skink *Cryptoblepharus virgatus* (Sydney, NSW)
96. Ocellated Skink *Ctenotus pantherinus* (Tennant Creek, NT)

97. Striped Skink *Ctenotus robustus* (Sydney, NSW)
98. Copper-tailed Skink *Ctenotus taeniolatus* (Sydney, NSW)

99

100

99. Cunningham's Skink *Egernia cunninghami* (Armidale, NSW)
100. Depressed Spiny Skink *Egernia depressa* (Port Hedland, WA)

101. Major Skink *Egernia frerei* (Mount Tamborine, Qld)
102. Hosmer's Skink *Egernia hosmeri* (Cloncurry, Qld)

103. Desert Skink *Egernia inornata* (Renmark, SA)
104. King's Skink *Egernia kingii* (Garden Island, WA)

105. Land Mullet *Egernia major* (Mount Tamborine, Qld)

106. Richard's Skink *Egernia richardi* (Little Nourlangie Rock, Kakadu National Park, NT)
107. Yakka Skink *Egernia rugosa* (Rockhampton, Qld)

108

109

108. Brown Rock Skink *Egernia saxatilis saxatilis* (Warrumbungle Ranges, NSW)
109. Black Rock Skink *Egernia saxatilis intermedia* (Coffs Harbour, NSW)

110

111

110. Spiny-tailed Skink *Egernia stokesii* (Broken Hill, NSW)
111. Night Skink *Egernia striata* (central Australia)

112

113

112. Tree Skink *Egernia striolata* (Goondiwindi, Qld)
113. White's Skink *Egernia whitii* (Bundeena, NSW)

114

115

114. Banded Skink *Eremiascincus richardsonii* (Turkey Creek, WA)
115. Garden Skink *Lampropholis guichenoti* (Sydney, NSW)

116

117

116. Weasel Skink *Lampropholis mustelina* (Sydney, NSW)
117. Spotted Skink *Leiolopisma ocellatum* (Lake St Clair, Tas.)

118. Red-throated Skink *Leiolopisma platynotum* (Sydney, NSW)
119. Two-toed Desert Skink *Lerista labialis* (Wilcannia, NSW)

120. Fire-tailed Skink *Morethia taeniopleura* (Darwin, NT)
121. Three-toed Skink *Saiphos equalis* (Sydney, NSW)

122. Douglas' Skink *Sphenomorphus douglasi* (Darwin, NT)
123. Murray's Skink *Sphenomorphus murrayi* (Coffs Harbour, NSW)

124. Black-tailed Skink *Sphenomorphus nigricauda* (Port Moresby, PNG)
125. Golden Water Skink *Sphenomorphus quoyii* (Sydney, NSW)

126. Yellow-bellied Skink *Sphenomorphus tenuis* (Goondiwindi, Qld)
127. Gunther's Skink *Tiliqua branchialis* (Halls Creek, WA)

128

129

128. She-oak Skink *Tiliqua casuarinae* (Gosford, NSW)
129. Pink-tongued Skink *Tiliqua gerrardii* (Gosford, NSW)

130. Central Blue Tongue *Tiliqua multifasciata* (Daly Waters, NT)
131A. Blotched Blue Tongue *Tiliqua nigrolutea* (Katoomba, NSW)

131B

31B. Blotched Blue Tongue *Tiliqua nigrolutea* (Rosebery, Tas.)

132

133

132. Western Blue Tongue *Tiliqua occipitalis* (Cobar, NSW)
133. Common Blue Tongue *Tiliqua scincoides scincoides* (Sydney, NSW)

134. Northern Blue Tongue *Tiliqua scincoides intermedia* (Darwin, NT)
135. Western Shingleback *Trachydosaurus rugosus rugosus* (Albany, WA)

136. Eastern Shingleback *Trachydosaurus rugosus asper* (Wilcannia, NSW)
137. Prickly Forest Skink *Tropidophorus queenslandiae* (Atherton, Qld)

138

139

138. The pandanus-fringed waterways of tropical Northern Territory provide a home for Merten's Water Monitor (*Varanus mertensi*) as well as the smaller Mitchell's Water Monitor (*Varanus mitchelli*), which occurs in this region alone. Among the lush vegetation along the water's edge the Northern Water Dragon (*Lophognathus temporalis*) will also be found.

139. The sandy plains of north-western Australia are host to a large and varied lizard population. Amongst the porcupine grass, which is the dominant feature of the landscape, live a number of geckos, including the White-striped Gecko (*Diplodactylus taeniatus*) and the Jewelled Gecko (*Diplodactylus elderi*), as well as Burton's Legless Lizard (*Lialis burtonis*) and many others. Because of the intense heat by day most of the inhabitants are nocturnal, though monitors such as the tiny Short-tailed Monitor (*Varanus brevicauda*) and the Central Sand Monitor (*Varanus gouldii flavirufus*) are active during the day.

140

141

140. This peculiar limestone formation in the Top End of the Northern Territory i
     the home of an uncommon lizard, the Ridge-tailed Monitor (*Varanu*
     primordius). The surrounding countryside is occupied by the Northern Blu
     Tongue (*Tiliqua scincoides intermedia*), and in the trees the Frilled Lizar
     (*Chlamydosaurus kingii*) and the Spotted Tree Monitor (*Varanus timorensi*
     similis) are abundant.
141. The blacksoil plains of western Queensland appear inhospitable, but a number o
     lizards have successfully adapted themselves to this harsh environment. Spencer'
     Monitor (*Varanus spenceri*) is one, a large, impressive lizard which excavates it
     burrow easily in the loose soil.

142

142. Along the rocky river gorges of north-western Australia the Long-nosed Water Dragon (*Lophognathus longirostris*) is the lizard most frequently observed. After nightfall geckos such as the Velvet Gecko (*Oedura marmorata*) emerge from rock crevices to forage for small insects.

143

144

143. The majority of lizards in the Sydney region take advantage of the shelter afforded by the weathering sandstone formations. The Copper-tailed Skink (*Ctenotus taeniolatus*) is perhaps the most common, and like White's Skink (*Egernia whitii*) burrows beneath rocks embedded in the sandy soil. Cunningham's Skink (*Egernia cunninghami*) is more at home in a tight rock crevice.

144. Like much of the dry interior of Australia, the saltbush plains of western New South Wales support a large population of lizards. By day the brightly coloured Painted Dragon (*Ctenophorus pictus*) darts swiftly among the stunted vegetation, and after dark the ground-dwelling geckos like the Central Knob-tailed Gecko (*Nephrurus levis levis*) emerge from their subterranean retreats.

145

145. The lizard population in near-impenetrable depths of the tropical rainforests of north-eastern Queensland is both prolific and spectacular. The slow-moving Boyd's Forest Dragon (*Gonyocephalus boydii*) relies on its superb camouflage to survive in the lush undergrowth. On the dark forest floor the secretive Prickly Forest Skink (*Tropidophorus queenslandiae*) lives amongst the thick layer of damp humus.

146

146. The extensive rock formations of the Arnhem Land escarpment and its outlier provide shelter for many lizards, some of which, like Richard's Skink (*Egernia richardi*), are found nowhere outside the region. Because of the stifling daytime temperatures most lizards are either nocturnal, or favour the cooler hours of early morning and late afternoon.

Index